# Mutiny
# in Paradise

by

MARGARET WAY

*Harlequin Books*

TORONTO • LONDON • NEW YORK • AMSTERDAM • SYDNEY

Original hardcover edition published in 1977
by Mills & Boon Limited

ISBN 0-373-02174-7

Harlequin edition published June 1978

PRINTED IN U.S.A.

# CHAPTER ONE

HE arrived at the hospital, much repressed, walking with his long stride down the corridors, until he found the room where Beth lay. She looked up expectantly, as though recognising his footsteps, and lifted a frail hand. He went to her swiftly, his heart giving a great bound.

'Hi! How goes it today?'

'Not so badly!' She smiled at him, beauty still in her wasted face.

He kept hold of her hand between both his own, sinking into the chair at the side of her bed and leaning forward to speak to her, because this was a public ward and those patients who did not have visitors seemed to fix their gaze and their attention on the patients who did. It was pitiful that Beth should be here. Unthinkable! In a kind of rage he had spoken to the Sister-in-charge about having her shifted to a private room, a room he would gladly pay for, but Beth insisted she preferred company, even dreaded the idea of being on her own. It was probably true anyway, as the steely gaze of the Ward Sister implied, that she was receiving the best of care and attention right where she was.

Beth was his cousin. In another lifetime they had loved one another passionately, but both their families had drawn together strongly to prevent any chance of a marriage between them. Beth had remained in their home town to marry someone her family approved of, a good man as it happened who had given his life somewhere in Vietnam; he, disenchanted, had roamed the

5

world, a drifter, turning his hand to anything before the McGoverns invaded and took over his life. Now he was a rich man because of them. Not enormously rich like the family, but doing extremely well.

It seemed important to him now that Beth should share in his tremendous good fortune. He had lost track of her over the long years, but he had never forgotten her, just as one never forgets one's first love. Beth hadn't forgotten him either, because it had been she who had written him begging him to pay her this one visit. He hadn't been difficult to trace this past ten years. Anyone who played a part in Big Bob McGovern's affairs periodically found themselves written up in the papers. Beth had needed someone and in the extremity of her anxieties she had written to him for help.

His strong brown hand touched her cheek. 'When you're out of here . . .' he said, feeling like crying.

'No.' She looked him straight in the eyes. 'This is terminal, my dear. I've come to terms with it, but I haven't told the children.'

'But surely there's *something*, Beth!'

'Only to look after the children. I waited too long. I was frightened and I waited too long. It's the same terrible story. One has to act fast with cancer. Only now I know I'm dying can I face up to the truth—a hollow sort of victory!'

'Beth!' He bowed his head over their joined hands. There seemed no way to comfort her. But she had gone far beyond comfort. She was facing the ultimate experience with all her courage, not raging and hating but with a controlled resignation, physically exhausted by pain. 'If only I had known earlier. If only I could have looked after you!' he said simply. 'I'm a rich man. Remember how your father used to say I'd never amount to anything? No one had any faith in me in those days. I was the natural target for all the sticks and stones. Anyway, money means nothing. I never wanted it, it just happened.'

'How? Tell me?' She smiled at him, weeping inside for the time that was slipping away from her.

His face had a bleak look as though he too felt overwhelmed by some terrible sense of loss. 'Chance,' he said slowly. 'One of those chance encounters that change lives. I'd been cruising round the South Pacific for years, taking a job here and there, but mostly the boat, when I put into Cairns to do a little blue marlin fishing off the Reef. It was almost as though I was brought there at that point in my life. I met Bob McGovern and started out on a new way of life. We talked a lot, fished a lot and drank one another under the table, and by the time I sobered up I found I was working for the man. Even when he was slapping around in his old gear I always knew I was talking to Someone, though he never said a word about himself. The McGoverns were the key to everything. Their interests are vast, anything from a tin mine to a coral island—anywhere there's money to be made. That's the canny Scot. You even have to slice through Bob's accent, and he came out to Australia as a lad of thirteen. He went to work then. I guess Bob is the biggest success story of the Far North. How to make millions from scratch!'

'But he's an old man now,' said Beth.

'Seventy-eight. But the dynasty will go on. They always do, given the right kind of people. Bob's son, Cameron, was killed in a mining accident. Nearly broke the old fellow up as nothing else could, but he rallied for Cal's sake; that's his grandson, Robert Calvin McGovern. We'll be hearing a lot about him. As far as I can see he's even an improvement on the old man. Cal can't do a thing wrong, which is why he'll find it easy to take over when Big Bob's gone. A lot of people are depending on Cal. A lot of highly successful enterprises, a lot of jobs!'

7

'You sound as though you admire him?'

He nodded. 'I do, enormously. He's the kind of man who could make his mark at any time, at any place. A tough, sardonic personality, hard-headed as blazes. Even as young as he is, he seems to put most of our competitors at an instant disadvantage. All deliberate, of course, a mixture of charm and aggressiveness. Bob is tremendously proud of him, though they have some great clashes from time to time. Cal doesn't swing on his heel as he used to when he was younger. He just stands there until Bob backs down. It's fascinating to watch.' He smiled. 'Both of them are big men and they survey one another down the same falcon's beak of a nose. The shouting and Bob smashing his fist down on the table! He can *really* roar, and the thicker the oaths, the quieter Cal gets. I'm always there and for the most part you could say I enjoy myself. I can see both sides and I can see how alike they are.' He laughed softly and Beth joined him, her dark green eyes full of a tender light. She felt as close to him as all those years ago, with never a family feud and great agitation between them.

His eyes travelled over her fine-drawn face. In some mysterious way it was still the face of the girl he had loved, yet it was a death-mask. He felt tears sting the back of his eyes, but he wasn't ashamed of them, for he was a man who had never kept his emotions under lock and key. 'I still love you, Beth!' he said, knowing it was true.

'You're not seeing me at my best!' she joked.

'You're still a lovely woman. I've never seen your colour hair anywhere.'

'You will very soon. Deborah is coming this afternoon.'

'Then I'll recognise her straight away.'

'I'm not going to cry. I'm not going to give in!'

'My girl!' Their hands linked together and there was a small silence.

'God sent you to me, Tommy!' she whispered.

'No one but you has ever called me Tommy!' he smoothed back her hair, trying to speak lightly. 'T.J. or Reynolds or Tom, but never Tommy!'

'They don't know you like I did. *Do!*' Beth corrected herself.

'You know I'll see to everything. I can't bear to speak about it ...'

'But we must. Deborah will be all right; she's very sensitive, but he's strong. Chris is the one I worry about. He needs time and attention. He has learning problems, and he's not clever at school as Deb was. In fact he's a most reluctant student, and it's so important in a boy.'

'Some children need a little time to develop, Beth. He's only ten years old. Probably he hasn't found a single thing to absorb his interest.'

'*Cars!*' she said, and smiled. 'He has a great interest in cars. Unfortunately they're not part of the curriculum. He needs a strong hand.'

'Most boys do!'

'I'll never see him grow to be a man,' she said sadly.

'Trust him to me. I swear I'll look after him like my own and dearest Beth, and I positively have a strong hand for an enthusiastic paddling if needs be!'

'He hasn't the slightest idea how ill I am.'

'And Deborah?'

'Deborah sees many things that are never said. She loves her brother and she'll never leave him, but she's so young herself.'

'Nineteen,' he replied. 'You were the same age when I left.'

'I carried a torch for a long time.'

'You weren't the only one.'

'Yet you never married?'

'I was denied the one girl I loved. I've known plenty of women, Beth, I can't take any credit for being a saint, but I've never met another woman I had a special feeling for—a tenderness, a protectiveness. The passion I had for you.'

'Have you been happy?'

'Who's happy?' he murmured.

'You're a very successful man, Tommy. That's important. You have your health and your strength. You're a very attractive man. Many women must have wanted to marry you.'

'Yes,' he said, and smiled at her, 'I could still find a wife in a flash. But now I see you again I know I never really got over you. Haunting women are the best and the worst kind.'

Very gently she stroked his hand. 'Could you give me a drink of water, please, Tommy? My throat is always so terribly dry.'

'Am I tiring you?'

'No, no!'

He stood up swiftly, a tall, heavily-built man, but very light on his feet, moving back to the stainless steel trolley and filling a glass tumbler from the water jug on it. 'Let me help you, Beth!' He half propped her up, then passed her the glass, watching her while she drank from it before he lowered her gently back on to the pillows. 'Better?'

'Yes, thank you!' Her hand touched her temple. 'I'm about due for my knock-out drop.'

'Is it so bad, Beth?'

'Bearable. It's a great comfort to have you here. Since the verdict was made final I've been almost desperate. Deb would try, but she could never rear Chris on her own. He would drain her youth and her energies. My Chris is a handful. I should be alive to protect him. Once I'm dead he will hardly remember me in a few years' time.'

'Don't, Beth!' he said, and stared at the white sheet. 'You need never feel desperate again. I'm here!'

She turned her head back along the pillow, seeking now to comfort him. 'I know—and listen, Tommy, it's enough!'

A young girl coming to the wide doorway of the ward caught the burning look in his fine dark eyes. It moved her deeply and for a moment she struggled against a flood of tears. She knew who he was; he even looked familiar, with a strong look of Grandfather Reynolds who had died. Her mother she could scarcely bear to look at, so blinding was her love and fear of losing her. The slight wasted figure hardly made any impression on the bed, the once beautiful glowing face was totally drained of colour with not even a shadow of its former vitality.

She wasn't a fool. Even before she had tackled Doctor Berryman she had known her mother was dying. She would never leave the hospital, never come home. A storm of grief hit her each night, but she could never show it before her mother. Deborah lifted her head and went forward, her hand outstretched.

'Cousin Tom!'

He came to his feet with a sense of amazement, his strong confident face unexpectedly youthful beneath a thick thatch of prematurely grey hair. The years slipped away from him. It was like meeting his young love all over again. Beth, before the long rush of the years, before suffering had marked her. He had never seen another woman like Beth until now. It was almost a miracle. He reached out his arms and Deborah went into them, smiling, welcoming him. A dark, glowing red rosebud on a far from sturdy stalk.

'You could never be anyone but Beth's daughter!'

'There now, I've met you!' She looked up, blinking the tears from her dark green eyes. 'I've heard so much about you. Now I know why Mamma loved you.'

'My dear child!' Overwhelmed, he turned back to Beth. 'How beautiful she is, Beth. It's just like meeting you all over again. I can't explain the sensation. It's remarkable!'

Beth nodded contentedly, and for a moment the pain lifted. 'You wouldn't think so now, but yes, I did look just like that!'

Deborah went to her mother quickly, kissing her cheek and pressing her frail shoulder. 'You still do!' she said, softly fierce. 'Even better—enriched and nobler. There's no comparison!'

Beth scrutinised her daughter's face with intense concentration as though she had to carry its memory into eternity. 'Deborah!' she said, relaxing her hand in her daughter's.

'Yes, darling?'

'Nothing. Just Deborah!' Beth answered. 'Do you know your mother is proud of you?'

With their two heads close together, Tom could see how illness had stripped the dark fire from Beth's beautiful hair; once it had been the same glowing rich red as her daughter's. Thick, heavy hair, expertly cut and shaped, falling to the shoulders with lots of curl and deep natural waves. Romantic, luxurious hair with a life of its own. Beth's had been the same, and all at once the pain in his chest became tighter. He stared at them, both their faces shining with the radiant love each felt for the other.

'I'd have recognised you, Deborah, in any part of the world. The resemblance is so close!'

'Then I've been blessed.' Deborah touched her mother's cheek gently. 'How is it today?'

'Much better!' Beth said with a faint colour. 'I'm happy, darling, and I'm not alone!'

And strangely it was true, Beth thought, with the end very near. Somehow her faith and her suffering had taught her to die. All that was left to do for her had been done. Tommy would look after the children. She would safely leave them in his hands. Tommy could take care of and control a growing boy. He would ensure Chris a future, her darling son, her baby, he wouldn't have to struggle alone. Chris wasn't gifted like Deborah. He would need help.

Beth was filled with a perfect gratitude. There was nothing to hold her now. The Creator could release her from her pain, though even pain had its value. She had learned a lot these past six months. She had counted every beat of her heart. She had been conscious of her every breath, when once years had flown past regardless. Her precious and unique possessions, her children, had occupied her every waking thought. Writing to Tommy had been the best thing she could have done. He had come at once like a special answer to her prayers. She no longer asked why —her beliefs gave her peace. If God wished to call her, that was that.

Her life had had quality—not a great deal of quantity, but *meaning*. She had always acted responsibly and she had an absolute faith in Tommy, not only because he *was* Tommy, but because he had always had a deeply protective nature. They had never understood that. Tommy had been so very vulnerable in the old days, so *proud*! and the family had been almost cruel to him, prepared to let him roam the world. They had never known precisely what kind of a man he was or could be. Now he had taken all the terrors of dying away from her; the children would be safe. She had always judged Tommy correctly, like his friends, the McGoverns.

Beth wondered what they were like. If she were given one other wish she would like to meet them. It did seem to matter, for Deborah and Chris would be spending a good part of their lives moving in the McGoverns' world. Their very position and their importance to Tommy ensured that. The McGoverns were involved without even knowing, and she hoped fervently that they would be kind to her children, but Tommy would see to that.

Tommy would keep them close to him after her death. Months ago she couldn't even think of it. She used to close her eyes and scream inwardly. Who wanted to think of their own funeral? Now the dread had gone. What was going to happen would happen. She could barely cope with the pain, anyway. Each time Deborah came Beth had the certain feeling that her daughter was reading that message in her eyes.

For a short time they were to be united by a feeling of great closeness while Deborah gave her mother what little news there was to catch up on and asked Tom questions about himself which he answered lightly, willing Beth just a flutter of his own abundant vitality. She laughed at him anyway, and offered a few comments of her own, content for the most part to hold her daughter's hand. They had perhaps a brief twenty minutes before a young nurse, all health and deftness, came to stand at the foot of the bed.

'How's my favourite patient today?' There was warmth and kindness in the brisk voice.

'So well and happy I don't really need that injection!'

'Oh, that's wonderful but I'll give it to you just the same. Ready, dear?'

Beth tried to smile and Deborah, her heart pounding, sprang out of her chair so that the nurse could come to the head of the bed. 'Just another minute or so!' she said, looking at Deborah and Tom rather piercingly before the nurse plunged the needle home with a gentle face, smiling into Beth's eyes with much more than professional compassion. Terminal cases upset her, but it was a matter of discipline to keep her feelings under control. This patient was as lovely as she was brave: Mrs Beth Nugent was dying and she knew it well.

'Right, now!' she said with a slight smile. 'You'll rest easy tonight.'

'Thank you, Nurse. I know you come around often to see me.'

'And I'll see you tomorrow!' the nurse said, her eyes fixed on Beth's chart. 'You ought to say good afternoon to your visitors. I suggest a nice little nap.'

Deborah and Tom got through their farewells, each trying desperately not to let their feelings show, but their thoughts were the same. They knew all there was to know, all but the exact amount of time Beth had left.

'Take care, dearest Beth!' Tom said urgently. 'You're in all our thoughts. I'll come and see you tomorrow.'

'Goodbye, Mamma!' Deborah's brilliant green eyes were enormous in her taut white face. There was no bargain she could make with anyone for her mother's life. Her dilemma was insoluble.

Conscious of the despair in that beautiful young face, Tom drew her back against his shoulder. She was a tall girl, but he stood head and shoulders above her. Beth looked back at them with unassailable serenity. 'Goodbye, my dear ones! You've no idea how much pleasure it gives me to see you together. Kiss my boy for me, Deb. He needs lots of loving attention. I know you'll both look after him!'

Deborah couldn't stand it. She moved involuntarily, and half supporting her too-slender frame, Tom moved to the door. Looking back at Beth he knew he would be put to the test very soon. There and then he committed himself to his responsibility, and vowed to take care of Beth's children just as well as he knew how. It was in his power to give them everything they could possibly want save their mother's continuing presence. He was happy and proud that Beth had sought him out; perhaps it was the reason why he had carried her in his heart all these years. They had always belonged together, he and Beth. Now her children would need sustaining. It was Beth's gift to him that he should be the one to do it.

He turned and saluted her and a great wave of love and trust seemed to flow between them. He could feel Deborah trembling, but she too lifted her hand though she could say nothing more. It was a beautiful moment and Tom knew he would treasure it.

Neither of them was to see Beth alive again, for she died quietly in her sleep just before dawn. The premonition strong in him, Tom had not returned to his hotel, but moved into Beth's home to be with his charges and remained there a week, attending to everything, before offering them what Beth had so earnestly desired, the shelter of his own home and guardianship.

Under the weight of their profound grief and knowing their mother had wanted it, they welcomed Tom's suggestion out of pure defeat. It didn't seem to matter anyway where they went and Tom was their cousin. They would all pull together as best they could. They didn't understand then that Cousin Tom, so gently authoritative, was a rich and important man and closely connected to one of the State's financial giants. A full knowledge was to come later when they went north and entered the McGoverns' world.

## CHAPTER TWO

THE last person Deborah expected to meet them at the airport was a girl about her own age; or perhaps a few years older, it was hard to tell. As they moved through the gate and into the terminal building the girl suddenly dislodged herself from the waiting crowd, her narrow glance skimming inscrutably over Deborah and Chris before she called Tom's name with a thrill of pleasure and welcome:

'T.J.!'

'Marisa!' Tom's rather stern expression broke up and he veered across to her, smiling and holding out his hand. 'Surely you haven't come to meet us?'

'What else?' the girl said gaily, indisputably pleased to see him. 'Eve couldn't make it. She had a hairdressing appointment she simply couldn't break. She wants to look her best for you.'

'I've never seen her looking anything else but great!' Tom said gallantly, still holding the girl's hand and pressing it affectionately. 'Really, this is very nice for us, Marisa. Wonderful! I'm hoping you and Deborah here will be the best of friends. Deb,' he said, his eyes softening as they rested on Deborah's pale young face, 'this is the daughter of a very good friend of mine, Eve Mangan. Marisa, these are my young cousins, Deborah and Chris. They've come to make their home with me.'

'Yes, I know. Cal told us!' Marisa said rather deliberately, smiling with a complete lack of goodwill at Deborah and ignoring Chris's shy, gruff hello.

17

'Cal's back, then?' Tom was asking.

'He won't be back until this afternoon!' Marisa responded with a fine edge of excitement and possessiveness in her husky voice. 'With the contract secure, wouldn't you know. He really enjoys himself, does Cal!'

'The big wheeler-dealer!' Tom seconded, and laughed softly in his throat. 'The Lord only knows how he managed to pull that one off so soon. He had a lot of opposition.'

'That's fuel to the fire with Cal. His grandfather is very pleased.'

'Yes indeed! I don't see why he shouldn't be. Cal's ready now to move to the head of the table.'

Marisa meanwhile was staring at Deborah with an undisguised lack of sympathy for all the set smile on her pert, triangular face. She was petite but shapely, with a lovely golden tan that made her dark eyes and hair more attractive than ever, huge sunglasses pushed back over her sleek, short hairstyle, and was superbly but casually turned out in an expensive sundress and thin, strappy sandals.

Even through her multiple layers of grief and reserve, Deborah was conscious that Marisa resented her on sight. It made her neither happy nor unhappy, sealed off as she was in her own private vacuum. Invariably, however, her own appearance was making an impression, and Marisa lost her brittle smile.

'So you've come to live with Tom?' she said in playful challenge. 'Aren't you the lucky ones?'

It seemed so out of place, so inappropriate, that Deborah shook her head wordlessly, so vulnerable, so deeply saddened that she couldn't see anything as a stroke of good fortune. Abruptly Tom put his arm around her with an attractive gesture of comfort and protectiveness that Marisa was quick to seize on. Her dark brown eyes set hard and her full mouth tightened, making her look nearer her real age, twenty-five.

'If you want to get the luggage, T.J., I'll take Deborah and her brother out to the car. Don't be too long. It's so terribly hot, and with Deborah so pale and red-haired, I don't imagine she'll enjoy our climate!' With a complete about-face she took Deborah's arm with a charming air of friendliness. 'Come with me. We'll have you home soon. You look absolutely *exhausted*!'

'Chris!' Deborah called to her brother who was preparing to follow Tom, then when she saw he was in one of his irritating, obstinate moods she broke Marisa's grasp, excusing herself to go after the small running figure.

She called his name again and he turned his head, checking in his flight. 'Please, Chris!' she said, catching up with him, 'be a good boy!'

'I don't *like* her!' he said, glowering belligerently. 'I want to go with Tom.'

'Please, darling!' she begged almost desperately, her head pounding from the long flight and her anguished week of grief.

'Oh, all right!' Chris shrugged his narrow shoulders. 'I sure hope we don't see much of her. She's a real bitch.'

'Don't say that!'

'She is. She didn't even look at me or say my name.'

Deborah sighed, knowing that his charge was quite true. 'Some people don't take much notice of children, Chris. They don't see them as people as we do. Don't let her bother you. Be the man of the family and try to be nice to her. She's a friend of Tom's and she's looking this way.'

'Let her!' said Chris, continuing to scowl. 'My skin is all prickly, it's so hot!'

'You can have a shower the minute we get home,' promised Deborah.

'We haven't got a home any more, remember?' he said,

and a spasm passed over his good-looking little face. 'I hate everyone, Debby, I just want Mum!'

'Yes, darling, but God is taking care of her.'

'Do you really think He is?'

With an effort Deborah kept the tears out of her eyes. 'What kind of a question is that? You *know* He is. She'll never have a sick day again. She'll be young and beautiful all at once, and she'll be able to see how we're behaving.'

'Anyway, I like Cousin Tom!' Chris said, with a tormented little smile. 'Mum wanted us to come with him.'

'Yes, she did. She loved him and she trusted him, and so will we.'

'He promised me a bike!' Chris looked up at his sister, almost expecting her to give her disapproval. 'Mum would never let me have one.'

'Only because there was no place to ride it except the busy street!' Deborah took her brother's unprotesting hand to steer him back through the crowd. 'Everything will be different up here. Tom said the house is on a couple of acres and there's a swimming pool. You'll love it.'

'I'd only love it if Mum was here!' Chris said bleakly.

'She is here, you know!' Deborah said softly. 'She's right here beside us, like a guardian angel.'

'Then I wish we could see her.'

'Please, darling, try and help me!'

'Sure, Debby. I believe you.'

Staring straight ahead of them, they rejoined Marisa, who couldn't resist a comment:

'What are you two looking so frantic about?'

'Is that the way we strike you?' Deborah asked, as though she really sought an answer.

It seemed to disconcert Marisa for a moment, then she gave a tight smile. 'I think you know already how you strike me.'

'I don't understand.'

'You will. I thought Cal was joking at first when he told us about you.'

'Oh?' said Deborah with her arm round Chris's shoulders.

'I mean, we had absolutely no preparation. The whole thing is touchingly absurd.'

'I don't *like* you!' Chris announced with furious antagonism.

Marisa shrugged. 'Who cares! You haven't very good manners.'

'Neither have you!' Chris answered, his blue eyes glittering. 'You look just like a black cat. I hate cats!'

'Forward kid, isn't he?' Marisa drawled. 'Something of a problem, I imagine?'

'I expect he'll become even more so if you continue to goad him,' Deborah said in a slightly grimmer voice.

Chris came to a standstill and pulled out from under his sister's arm. 'I'm going to stay here until Tom catches up with us.'

'Suit yourself,' Marisa responded airily. 'I don't like insulting little boys anyway.'

'No, but you love yourself!' Chris burst out, characteristically determined to get the last word.

'If you want to stay there, stay there!' Deborah said hastily. 'Don't move until Tom comes through this door.'

'Leave the kid to figure it out for himself!' Marisa broke in again. 'You shouldn't be so over-protective. It's not good for them.'

'And would you know?' Deborah asked quietly, wishing only to wait for Tom herself.

'Well, kids are just kids, aren't they? Eve always taught me to be self-reliant. I never took up all her time. She didn't want that.'

'Chris is only ten years old and he has just lost his

mother—he didn't want that either. I'm all he has in the way of a mother. I think he's coping very well with his despair. Please try to remember that in your dealings with him.'

'I can see that kid is going to cause a lot of friction,' Marisa said for answer. 'You're not too much alike, are you?'

'You'll see when you know us better that we are.'

'Oh well!' Marisa said with dry resignation. 'He can be shoved off to a boarding school at least. It would do him the world of good, from the little I've seen. Did T.J. tell you he and Eve are very close friends?'

'There hasn't been time for Tom to tell me anything. We're here now, and believe me, we don't intend to interfere in Cousin Tom's life.'

'But you've done that already!' Marisa pointed out with harsh honesty. 'You may not have known it before, so I'll tell you now that my mother is absolutely devoted to T.J. In fact, she has no interest in any other man.'

Deborah turned her glowing head, no longer bemused. 'I can't see how we're going to change that!'

'Just by being here!' Marisa snapped. 'Cal was just as astonished as we were—T.J. arriving back with a couple of orphans! I mean, it was so utterly unexpected. I didn't even believe it until now. You're not a child; you don't need T.J. to look after you!'

'I can't leave my brother,' said Deborah.

'I suppose your mother put it to him?' Marisa challenged boldly.

Deborah put a trembling hand to her throbbing temple. 'Are you always like this? An *attacking* kind of person?'

'I'm just trying to get a few honest answers,' snapped Marisa. 'What are you doing here?'

'Forgive me, but I don't think you're entitled to any

explanations beyond the fact that we're here at my cousin's invitation. The last thing I expected was hostility in such a beautiful setting.'

'You surely couldn't have expected the long arm of friendship either. That would have been asking too much. Quite a lot of us are pretty suspicious of you.'

'I can't think why!' Deborah said wearily, thankful that Tom and Chris were coming their way.

'Oh, come now!' Marisa very nearly sneered. 'I hope you don't expect to reap the benefits of T.J.'s wealth!'

Deborah stood in silence, staring at her, then her beautiful head jerked up. 'The idea had never occurred to me. Nor was I aware that Cousin Tom was anything more than a successful businessman.'

'You don't need to lie to me!' Marisa said with a soft mirthless laugh. 'I guess your mother knew all there was to know about T.J. Why else would she have contacted him?'

'She knew his heart and mind, yes,' Deborah agreed quietly. 'Obviously you don't know just how close they were.'

'Until Cal told us we didn't even know you or your mother existed!' Marisa burst out with renewed malice. 'Cal definitely wasn't in favour of Tom's taking on a ready-made family.'

'Why should it affect him?'

'You'll find, Miss Green-Eyes, that Cal gives the O.K. on everything. He doesn't like stupid mistakes, and T.J. is part of the firm. Just the way Cal told us proves he doesn't go along with all this—you and your kid brother. Your mother must have put T.J. in an intolerable position. He's so dependable, so soft underneath, that she wouldn't have had much of a job.'

'What do you want me to say, Miss Mangan? That we'll turn around and go back on the next plane?'

'It would really be the smart thing to do, but no;

we're not completely heartless, you know, just practical. Stay for a holiday by all means. I can see you're frightfully run down. I take it you have a job of some sort?'

'You're very formidable for such a young woman!' Deborah observed with an awful sense of loneliness.

'You haven't met Eve yet!' Marisa smiled, showing her small white teeth.

'Which is perhaps fortunate at this stage. I'm sorry our presence is causing you both so much disturbance.'

'It was quite a shock, I can tell you. You could have stopped all this—you could have simply told T.J. you didn't want to come.'

'Yes, I could have, but it seemed right to do what my mother wanted.'

'Ah yes, your mother!' Marisa said with a bitter flash of her near-black eyes. 'Did she look anything like you?'

'Much, much better!' Deborah was almost on the point of collapse.

This seemed to occur to Marisa belatedly, for she put a steadying hand under Deborah's elbow. 'Are you all right? You've gone as white as a sheet.'

Deborah's instinctive withdrawal repudiated the other girl's momentary softening. 'Here's Tom now. Shall we go out into the air?'

'I'd see a doctor if I were you!' Marisa advised, looking back over her shoulder and waving at Tom. 'I hope you don't expect T.J. to sit about fussing over you. He's a very busy man.'

'I'll try not to bother him,' Deborah said tautly.

'Eve expects to see him tonight, understand?'

'Perfectly.'

'Good. Make it easy on yourself. Have a long luxurious holiday with all expenses paid, then go away. I have an idea you're a misfit anyway.'

'I don't think I'd have come, Miss Mangan, if I'd known you were going to meet us.'

'Nothing could have made me stay away,' rejoined Marisa. 'I was afraid you'd be stupid and treat us all to a boring display of your gratitude, but now I see you're not stupid at all!'

Deborah's dark green eyes suddenly flashed. 'Doesn't that make me all the more dangerous?'

'You may be beautiful,' Marisa said, 'I can see that, but Cal can spot a fake from miles off. It's really up to Cal how long you'll be permitted to stay here. I think that's wonderful!'

'And I think it improbable,' answered Deborah. 'You don't know Tom at all.'

'I know the McGoverns made him what he is today, and I know they could put him back right where they found him—at the bottom of the barrel.'

'As I said, you don't know Tom at all.'

'And you won't get the chance either,' Marisa said spitefully. 'You've got to step over my mother first.'

Deborah put up her hand to shade her eyes from the brilliant sunlight. 'All right, Miss Mangan, you wanted to upset me and you have. Like Chris, I'm going to wait here until Tom arrives.'

'Don't try and influence him against us! We've all been good friends for a very long while. You and your brother are our first disruptive elements.'

'I'm sorry you should feel like that. It was the last thing in the world I wanted or expected.'

'Perhaps,' Marisa agreed. 'Maybe it was your mother who forced the situation at that!'

'Please don't speak about my mother in that tone of voice,' Deborah said coldly, coming back to startling life. 'I won't take it, not from anyone.'

'Get a hold on yourself!' Marisa cried, genuinely startled, for the change in Deborah had been so great. 'I know how you feel, for God's sake, and you'd better understand how *we* feel. My mother has no intention of allowing you and your brother to wreck her plans, and don't try running straight to T.J. There'll be no future in that and you won't want to make things any more difficult for you. If T.J. surrendered to some kind of emotional blackmail, then it's up to his friends to get him out of it.'

'And you're his *friend*?' Deborah asked quickly, her green eyes so steady that Marisa looked away in anger.

'He's lived the best of his life with us. He was a nobody up until then.'

'You mean if you're not rich you don't count?'

'Well, it does make a difference, as you've already found out,' Marisa retorted. 'We're terribly sorry about it all really, but we're not going to sit still under this charming arrangement. For one thing, T.J. doesn't exactly look at you like a young cousin. Eve will spot that at once.'

Deborah stepped back immediately towards Tom, who was wheeling a trolley towards them laden with luggage. 'Good boy!' he was saying to Chris, who had put a balancing hand on the top piece. 'It's suddenly occurred to me that I'm out of shape. Once I would have walked off with all this under my arms.'

'I don't think anyone could do that, Uncle Tom!' Chris smiled up at him. 'But you're very strong, that's a fact!'

Marisa walked away briskly to where a big American car was parked and Tom, after one look at Deborah's pale face, followed her over, gesturing to Chris to run ahead the better to help.

'Boy, a Lincoln!' Chris exclaimed his eyes widening. 'I'd know them anywhere.'

'I'm a big man, I need a big car!' Tom answered him, smiling.

'This is the first run I've been able to give it!' Marisa told him as she watched him put the luggage into the boot then handed him the keys.

'Good for you! Now, young man, how would you like to sit up the front?'

'Thank you, Uncle Tom. Thanks a lot.'

'Pile in, Deborah!' Marisa said in a friendly fashion, opening up the back door. 'You'll like all that lovely room to yourself!'

'That's if you ever find me again.'

'You must be a millionaire, Uncle Tom!' Chris said in wonderment.

'I'm not too badly off, Chris. Now, let's get your sister home. It's been a long, long, week. Marisa dear, you're a sight for sore eyes!'

'Wait until you see Eve. She's making herself beautiful right this minute!'

Tom met Deborah's eyes in the rear vision and surprisingly he wasn't smiling; rather faintly harassed, from his long trip and the great change in his domestic arrangements, she imagined. She didn't know what the answer was and she was too spent to work it out just then. She lacked the strength and her natural youthful optimism.

As he held her eyes Tom's faint frown changed to a smile, a warm uncomplicated exchange, and thankfully she grasped that whatever his reaction of strain, she and Chris weren't the cause of it. It seemed a tremendous advantage and she tilted her head back on the opulent upholstery and tried to relax. Marisa had left her in little doubt of their welcome, but grief itself put up an impenetrable barrier. Chris, in front, was almost speechless with satisfaction, deeply impressed with his ride in a luxury car and the fact that Uncle Tom really owned it. It was left to Marisa to make conversation and this she did with great animation, smiling continually at Tom's intent profile.

Whether or not Deborah was sealed off quite definitely in her own vacuum didn't strike Marisa as important. She rattled on as though a glass partition divided the back of the car from the front, so Deborah sat apart, grateful for the cooling breeze that ruffled her hair. The sun had a brilliance and power she wasn't used to, but the countryside looked lush and green, shimmering in the heat haze, with great crimson poincianas making an archway across the highway; the flamboyant parasite, the bougainvillea, repeating itself endlessly in great tree-high drifts, the tulip trees breaking out their orange flowers that proclaimed in spectacular fashion the true tropical environment.

A car passed them going in the opposite direction and the driver, a woman, waved cheerfully. 'Ann!' Marisa said, waving back carelessly. 'I expect she's going back into town. How long is it now she's been chasing Cal?'

'I've seen plenty do that!' Tom murmured dryly. 'Haven't you?'

'A girl would be mad not to,' rejoined Marisa.

'I like Ann,' Tom said rather doggedly.

'Good for you!' Marisa wrinkled her pert nose. 'I like her too—she can be good company in small doses. She'll be at the party on Saturday night anyway. I don't know what makes her think she's qualified to handle Cal.'

Tom smiled at her. 'What I want to know is, who can?'

'He thinks *you're* extremely capable.'

'For which I'm more than grateful. How's the Old Man?'

'Pushing himself too hard. He missed you when you were away.'

'It was necessary, and there was little delay,' Tom said, low-voiced, his eyes for an instant on Deborah in the back seat. 'I didn't realise Cal would be away too. I'd like to know how he worked it with Alcan—Dodds is a cold-blooded old devil.'

'And as it happens he was no match for Cal.' Marisa

smiled. 'He can manipulate anyone. A combination of techniques, tough and charming. Aren't you glad about it?'

'Of course. Things move when Cal is about, and we have to move with him. If there's a lot of stress, there's a lot to be gained. Success can be frightening. One has to have the temperament.'

'You're joking!' Marisa began to laugh softly, faintly contemptuously, successful at no more than buying herself new clothes.

'No, actually I'm quite serious!' Tom answered good-naturedly. 'As many people are as afraid of being a success as of being a failure. I shouldn't wonder if a man isn't better off leading a peaceful mediocre existence, un-recognised by anyone.'

'But you must enjoy being rich, T.J.?' Marisa asked, looking at him closely.

'I was never in it for the money. I enjoy what it can buy me, of course, but mostly it's been proving myself to Bob, proving he judged me correctly. I really love that old man.'

Marisa threw her head back and laughed, a peculiarly mirthless sound. 'My, that's good! Most of us are scared stiff of him.'

'Oh yes, I know that,' Tom pondered, 'but they ob-viously don't see beyond the bark. Bob is a real man. A man to turn to for help. He's a hard man to beat, but he has a heart. He's a man of great tolerance and he has never betrayed a trust. I can only think of one other man who measures up to him, and that's his grandson.' He spoke absently. 'Of course Bob was always the boy's teacher. Almost a father. Cal never had a normal child-hood after his father was killed and his mother re-married; all he had was the Old Man. Big Bob was the truth and the law and provider. Is it any wonder they're so close?'

'Yes, the woman who marries Cal will have to know what she's getting into.' Marisa sighed. 'The Old Man misses nothing and he's not slow to give his opinion. Cal's thirty-four now, and he's still not married.'

'Which doesn't mean to say he ignores women!' Tom said dryly.

'No news!' Marisa sighed again as though she really meant it. 'He really ought to do something about putting us out of our agony. It's a crying shame, the way Cal wastes so much precious time.'

'Oh?' Tom grinned at her. 'I thought he was pretty fully occupied. Bob expects so much of him that a lesser man would simply head for the hills. Instead of which Cal moves from one commitment to the next. I'll tell you something, he's going to be an even bigger name in this State than Bob. He's brilliant, he works his insides out and he's the biggest persuader of the lot. Anyone who can fix Charlie Dodds and make it look easy is right on top of his world. There's a terrific opportunity now to land the contract with the government—how's it going there, Deborah? Not boring you, are we?'

She reached across and touched his shoulder. 'No. To begin with I'll have to learn about the people who are important to you.'

'Well, don't damned well look at Cal!' Marisa burst out impetuously, trying at the last moment to turn it into a joke. 'He's mine!'

'Yeah?' Tom looked sidelong at her. 'You might as well talk about owning a whole organisation.'

'Are you warning me, T.J.?'

'I wouldn't like to see you get hurt. When we're talking about Cal we're talking about a man no woman will ever own. He might own her, but she won't own him. He's too darned dominant, an extraordinary man.'

'I don't care what he is!' Marisa said, and laughed suddenly and not altogether humorously. 'I don't even care if he doesn't pay me too much attention. It's the quality of the time that counts. I want him and he knows it. It might be as well for Deborah to know it too. I haven't missed the fact that she's pretty, and Cal won't miss it either.'

'Not pretty, *beautiful*!' Tom said almost reverently. 'There's a long way in between.'

Marisa clapped her hands, a red patch on either cheek. 'Oh, lovely! It's certainly delightful to get a compliment. Aren't you pleased, Deborah?'

'That's very kind of you, Tom,' she said quietly, recognising Marisa's dazzling flash of jealousy.

Tom, however, had missed it, his dark eyes faraway and without their usual keen sparkle. 'I'm sure it's not the first time you've heard it. You're truly blessed, Deb, to have inherited your mother's looks. I regarded Beth as the most beautiful woman I've ever seen—no less beautiful with all the years in between. My dear, dear Beth!'

There was a little silence that Marisa broke in the same, bright challenging tone. 'Eve won't love you for that, T.J.!'

'You can believe it all the same,' Tom maintained gravely. 'How are you doing, young feller?' He tousled Christopher's dark head with a careless hand. 'You haven't said a word!'

'I've been thinking all right, Uncle Tom. This really spanks along, doesn't it? It's the biggest car I've ever been in. The next biggest was a Dodge, I suppose. Nigel owned it.'

'Who's Nigel?'

'A friend of Debby's. He's really gone on her.'

'And is Debby gone on him?' Marisa interjected gaily.

'Why don't you ask her?' Christopher offered, his head turned slightly away from her.

'I will. What's the answer, Deborah?'

'Simple friendship on both sides,' she replied.

'He's an ass about her really!' Christopher supplied for Tom's benefit, ignoring Marisa's avid interest from his other side.

'That will do, son,' Tom said lightly. 'Your sister is entitled to her privacy.'

'There's some truth in that, I suppose.' Marisa sighed regretfully. 'Forgive me, Deborah, if I like to ask questions, but there's so little we know about you and if we're all going to be seeing so much of each other I don't think it so unusual to expect a few answers.'

'I think you're horrible!' Chris declared, sitting bolt upright.

'Same here, little man!' Marisa retorted instantly.

'Chris, you can apologise for that.'

'All right, Uncle Tom, I will, but she'd better make sure she doesn't get a snitcher on Debby!'

'A snitcher? What's a snitcher?' Marisa demanded.

'*You* know!'

'Chris!' Deborah and Tom both said together.

The boy glanced at Marisa with some hostility then averted his eyes. 'I'm sorry,' he said, as though it well-nigh killed him.

'Manners!' Marisa clicked her tongue. 'Oh well, we'll soon correct them up here.'

'Listen, Marisa,' Tom said quietly, 'I'm not prepared to side with Chris. He's been impertinent, but on the other hand I think he's entitled to a little extra in the way of understanding and compassion. Why don't you both retire from the field?'

'I intend to!' Marisa said sweetly.

'Take my advice, son, and do the same.'

'Yes, sir, I promise. I only wanted to enjoy the ride anyway. She started it, asking questions and everything. There's something wrong with her. She scares me.'

'You could have fooled me,' Marisa replied instantly. 'Really, Deborah, you'll have your work cut out rearing this boyo!'

'I don't accept that at all,' Deborah answered, 'children are very perceptive. I will, however, speak to him when we get home.'

'Yes, you do that. Rouse yourself if you have to.'

A small pulse hammered at the base of Deborah's creamy throat, showing her distress. She sought for a quick change of subject and found it as the road curved to the left and rose fairly steeply, allowing them their first view of a very dramatic white house with a hilltop setting surrounded by velvet green lawns and blossoming poincianas and jacarandas in all their tropical splendour. It looked wonderful, like some luxurious compound with a broad avenue of royal palms leading right down to the massive wrought-iron gates, flanked by a high but airy ornamental fence with pointed finials and medallions and heavy white concrete pillars smothered in jasmine and an intermingling yellow-flowered vine.

'Gosh, that's a beaut house!' Chris burst out enthusiastically, his mood completely changed.

'The McGovern Estate!' Marisa pointed out in a proprietorial voice.

'The house sits on about six or seven acres, mostly to the rear overlooking the coastal ranges,' Tom added, slowing down the car so that they could better appreciate the dimensions of the house and the magnificent grounds.

'It's dazzling!' Deborah said sincerely. 'A tropical palace with a Spanish touch, just right for its setting.'

'The interior is even more luxurious,' Marisa told her. 'Terribly sophisticated but informal, if you know what I mean. The house is full of very important paintings and antiques and sculptures, but they're side by side with a totally modern look. It's tremendously stylish. The family entertains on the grand scale, of course, and there are always visitors from overseas. Friends, and relations and business associates.'

'Who mows all that lawn?' Chris asked in wonderment.

Tom looked at him with some amusement. 'Oh, there's quite a team to take care of things. Everything grows overnight in the tropics. Those same beautifully manicured grounds would be a wilderness in under a month. The grass alone needs daily attention.'

'Gee, it's fantastic!' said Chris, turning his head to view the house from another angle. 'Is your place anything like that, Uncle Tom?'

'Nothing so divine!' Tom laughed good-naturedly. 'The McGovern place is special, a showplace, very glamorous and extensive. It has to be—their position demands it. You'll like our place, though. It's restful and very private and we all share a beautiful setting. The richness of nature here is amazing. There's always something blossoming prolifically, and you'll be fascinated by the butterflies that swarm around the lantana. They're so big and beautiful that you won't believe it. There'll be plenty of room for you to move around in, Chris, and I have a swimming pool you're going to love!'

'It sounds great!' Chris said, touching Tom's arm in friendship. 'Debby can swim like a fish.'

'Another of her talents?' Marisa interjected, turning her head back to smile at Deborah. 'You don't happen to play the piano, do you? Nobody else around here can and there's a Steinway concert grand up at the house.'

'Does it matter exactly?' Deborah asked, meeting Marisa's dark eyes.

'Well, you'd be sure of a invite up to the house. The Old Man loves music. It's his one relaxation now that he doesn't go big game fishing anymore.'

'Then it seems as though the only thing to do is admit it.'

'You mean you actually *do* play?' Marisa demanded almost convulsively.

'There's hardly a thing Deb can't do!' Chris supplied with as much malice as pride, conscious of Marisa's displeasure.

Through the deep thick foliage they could catch glimpses now of beautifully secluded homes, and as the road unfurled seemingly for ever, Tom suddenly left the highway and turned into a wide smoth drive with banks of flowering shrubs on either side and took the car up to a two-storied home anyone might dream of owning. 'Home!' was all he said.

Double garage doors were thrown wide open and they could see in the darkened recess a high-slung little sports car that Marisa claimed at a glance. 'Now that I've seen you safely home again, T.J., I'll be going. Eve has a few little jobs lined up for me. You'll be seeing her tonight, of course?'

'Marisa dear, I don't know if I'll be able to manage it!'

'But you'll have to!' She threw her arm back over the seat. 'You'll excuse him, Deborah, won't you?'

'Why, of course! Tom knows the last thing we want is to change his life.'

'I suggest we all go inside,' Tom said, and drove into the empty bay and cut the engine. 'It's been a long flight, and Deb and Chris must be tired.'

Marisa opened her door and got out, standing poised with one hand on the roof. 'If it's all right with you, T.J., I won't come in. You'll find everything in order. Eve checked the place over yesterday. See you tonight!'

'Will we go up to that side door, Uncle Tom?' Chris was asking.

'No, we'll go around the front!' Tom stopped and

went round to Marisa, putting his hand on her shoulder. 'Thank you for coming out to meet us. I appreciate it. Tell Eve I'll ring her just as soon as we've settled in.'

'She'll be glad to hear from you. She's missed you. So long, Deborah, Chris! I expect we'll be seeing a lot of one another.' Marisa gave a little elegant wave of her hand, then slipped into the driving seat of the yellow sports car and hunted up the keys from her bag. 'By the way, T.J., Cal is expecting a call as well.'

'Of course he is.' Humour lines flared out from Tom's fine dark eyes. 'After I've had a drink he might get one.'

Marisa turned on the ignition and the car moved smoothly out into the sunlight, exuding silent power. Chris, on Deborah's other side, couldn't help admiring it. 'Gee, are you all rich, Uncle Tom?'

'Delightful, isn't it?' Tom said wryly. 'Marisa's father had considerable interests in this part of the world, and after he died Eve sold out to the McGoverns for a comfortable small fortune. Marisa is usually very warm and friendly. She wasn't quite herself today for some reason. I would like you, Chris, to be always polite to her. You're growing up now and good manners are important.'

'She doesn't like us, Uncle Tom. You can see that!'

'I can feel something,' Tom admitted. 'Ah well, you can't win 'em all. Welcome to my small corner of peace. I hope you'll be very happy here.'

Chris threw his arms around him with a flourish, and when Tom looked down he could see that he was crying. 'Now, now, son, you start that and you might find I'll join you!' He began to laugh softly, his hand on the boy's thick, glossy hair, and after a minute Chris recovered himself sufficiently to take both Tom and his sister by the hand and walk out into the golden sunshine, leading the way to the front door.

'Thank you, Tom!' Deborah said softly, smiling at

him over Chris's head. She looked enchanting, for that smile had been rare.

'It's what I want,' he assured her. 'I only hope that in time it's what you'll want too. A home is nothing without love in it, children. Sometimes I've felt quite lost. Is it any wonder I wanted to bring Beth's children here?'

A jacaranda, drenched in lavender, seemed to fill the front garden and Deborah looked at it, the familiar ache around her heart lessening.

'How lovely!' The tree seemed to welcome her and she didn't want to go beyond that moment in its little oasis of forgetfulness. But there was always the future, and she had to face it. Tom in his generosity had offered them comfort and shelter, acknowledging, if only briefly, that he too needed something life had hitherto denied him. Beth was the link that joined them, and her tender memory would show them the way.

# CHAPTER THREE

WHEN Marisa arrived home, Edna, their housekeeper told her her mother was resting in her room after a gruelling three-hour session at the hairdresser's. Marisa didn't want to disturb her mother, for Eve always became very irritable if she was disturbed from a sleep, but it was important. Eve had to know about this totally unreal situation that was developing, far, far worse than either of them had considered.

Marisa herself was filled with a storm of outraged emotions, feeling that some very real threat was being posed for both herself and her mother. She hadn't even begun to analyse the intensity of dislike, almost hate, that she felt for T.J.'s ready-made family; she only knew he had in some way betrayed them. Men were such fools! Even clever, successful men like T.J. He should have known better than to be blackmailed by some ghost from his past, the haunting, so-beautiful Beth.

Marisa shuddered, remembering his very words, the thrill of genuine feeling that had run through his voice when he had spoken about his dead cousin. Eve would turn ugly when she heard about this girl, Beth's daughter. Eve was a woman of strong emotions and her soul had some dark places. Marisa admired and feared her mother, and never once established in her conscious mind that she did not love her. She lived only to keep on her mother's good side, and was still, at twenty-five, unsure of how best to go about it. Eve was a very positive woman and she considered it unnecessary to make a friend of

38

her daughter, a state of affairs that had hardened over the years to a kind of autocracy which would come to an end only if Marisa married. Marisa's fruitless search for deep maternal love had now changed itself into a constant striving to win her mother's respect, when Eve lacked the capacity for more than a benign indifference at best and a belittling, unbelievably petty tyranny when her own day was spoilt.

It was not surprising therefore that Marisa approached her mother's bedroom almost timidly, tapping softly on the door and evoking no response. She bit her lip and knocked again a little louder, and this time her mother's decidedly edgy voice retaliated:

'Who *is* it?'

Marisa stood there for a moment almost in an attitude of simple-mindedness, then she turned the doorknob and went in. Though she was sharp-tongued in her own circle, it never once occurred to her to answer with something amusing, let alone tart. Her mother swung up abruptly with a complete lack of goodwill, and her eyes sharpened at the look of bitterness and upset that now showed in Marisa's petite golden-skinned face.

'I imagine this has something to do with those damned orphans?' she shot at her daughter.

'Yes.' Marisa answered equally abruptly, then stood in the centre of the carpet as though paralysed.

'Is that all you can say?' Eve snapped back irritably. 'I left instructions not to be called for another hour.'

'I'm sorry,' Marisa apologised, and the sincerity was unmistakable, 'but I felt you should know.'

'Well then, tell me for God's sake!' Eve invited, swinging her long shapely legs down to the floor and leaning forward to select a cigarette from the ivory box on the bedside table. She put it to her full lips, lit it in a short, efficient burst and took a deep draw before she waved her hand for her daughter to begin her recital.

'Everything was not in order, I take it?' she asked with considerable asperity.

'They're quite dreadful!' Marisa almost moaned.

'In what way? Honestly, you come in here like a little madwoman, full of your fancies, only to stand there apparently speechless! If it's not too difficult for you, I'd like to hear.'

'The girl, Deborah, is very beautiful!'

'Pardon me,' her mother answered, her voice carrying a sting, 'but would you know?' There was a suggestion in Eve's face that she had been offered a personal insult.

'I've never seen a better-looking girl!' Marisa said guiltily.

'My God!' Eve began to blow jets of smoke through her nose. 'Can't you unbend a little for my sake? She's beautiful, you've obviously made up your mind about that, but I'll reserve my opinion until I see her. Yours doesn't carry that much weight.'

'T.J. thinks so too,' said Marisa defiantly. 'Apparently he was obsessed with her mother.'

The dark glitter in Eve's eyes intensified. She reached over and viciously stubbed out her cigarette as though the taste maddened her, then she turned back to her daughter. 'What kind of nonsense are you talking?'

'He said so himself. He said his cousin Beth was the most beautiful woman he'd ever seen, no less beautiful for all the years in between. "My, dear, dear Beth!" That's exactly what he said, and it sounded like an agony of regret.' Marisa stood there uncertainly as though the thought had only just struck her. 'I'm very fond of him, you know. He has a kind of tenderness. He's lost quite a bit of weight in one week and he's very protective of Beth's children.'

'Already?' Eve demanded.

'Already. T.J. is in his prime, he's still a big, hand-some man, and the girl is supposed to be the image of her mother. His face changes every time he looks at her. Even his voice softens.'

'Are you sure you're not just exaggerating?' Eve demanded, bending down for her shoes and feeling infuriated enough to hurl them at her daughter.

'I'm simply telling you the situation as I saw it, Eve. I apologise if it was a mistake.'

'What else is this paragon besides being monotonously beautiful? Blonde hair and big blue eyes, that never fails!'

Marisa stared back at her mother and saw fright behind the taut, imperious expression, so that she shook her own head helplessly. 'She has hair like a dark flame and green eyes to go with it.'

'Has she now?' Eve murmured, softly vicious. 'And you watched them together. Men are notoriously susceptible to a pretty face, and Tom's no different from any other man. Besides, he couldn't afford to take more than a family interest in such a child.'

'Plenty of things happen to nineteen-year-old girls!' Marisa said a little curtly. 'Anyway, don't upset yourself on that score—I don't think she's even vaguely aware of T.J. in that way. She's obviously upset about her mother and she's one of those remote types, you know, who look right through and beyond you.'

Eve was standing in front of the window now, tall and very rigid, the force of her arrogant personality triumphing over the gracious, sophisticated façade. 'It doesn't matter what she is,' she said grimly. 'I'll allow no chit of a girl to get in my way. I've given Tom two full years of my life. I won't give him up now, and I won't tolerate any growing attachments to any conniving young people he can ill afford to have in his house. What about the boy?'

Marisa relaxed immediately. 'A real brat,' she said

disparagingly. 'He took one look at me and told me he didn't like me.'

'I suppose you were stupid enough to show your dislike in front of Tom?' her mother challenged her.

'Wouldn't you if a child was so obviously rude?'

'My dear girl, you surprise me! No child has ever been rude to me. I don't invite or expect that kind of thing. I can't for the life of me imagine why you should bracket us together. It's quite absurd.'

'Yes, I suppose so!' Marisa murmured, flushing a little and thinking she had better leave any more comments unspoken. She crossed the room and gently remarked how very much she admired Eve's new hairstyle.

Eve fingered a deep glossy wave and suddenly looked very calm. 'Yes, it turned out pretty well considering Paul wasn't there. Personally, pet, I don't know if you're bright enough for me to rely on your judgment or instincts or whatever. Are you sure you're not just frightened for yourself? You want Cal, but you haven't got the guts or the know-how to really go after him. If I were only just a few years younger...'

'You know perfectly well you look about twenty-eight!' Marisa said soothingly, a lie so patent that it was astonishing Eve smiled, but she did, a handsome but undeniably vintage beauty.

'Well, not twenty-eight, I'm afraid, but certainly the early thirties, and that's how I feel!' Eve half turned towards the long mirror and went through the ritual of studying her tall, well proportioned figure. 'I'm telling you, girl, there's not one chance in a million of Tom's getting away from me. I've spent too much time on him, and I'm just about ready to bring him to the point of marriage. This Deborah—such an odd Biblical name—we'll dispose of in the nicest, most genteel way possible. It's an unlovely fact, of course, that we might be stuck with the boy for a few years yet, but there are plenty of excellent boarding schools.'

'You're absolutely right!' Marisa said smartly, with the automatic co-operation she had long been programmed for.

'As usual!' Eve breathed complacently, and turned to her daughter for a moment. 'Tom did say he was coming tonight?'

Marisa hesitated for a moment, unwilling to say anything jarring. 'He said he would ring!'

'Poor Marisa!' her mother mocked her. 'You're always so interested in pleasing me. I'll be the first one to say thank you for going out and meeting Tom for me, but really, darling, you have no subtlety, no real capacity for handling situations. In fact, I've suddenly realised you're uncommonly like your father.'

'I can't see why you go out of your way to criticise Father!' Marisa burst out on a sudden wave of loyalty to the memory of her kindly and well-respected father.

'Oh, do stop it! You're making me scream with nerves. Marrying Dennis was quite the worst thing that ever happened to me. Don't make me think you're an even worse penalty. If you really want to make me happy and proud and pay back all the time and effort I've put into you, you'll win yourself a real man, like Cal. I'm more than capable of looking after my own affairs and I don't go around dramatising things either. I suppose you forgot to pick up my skin lotion?'

'I'll get it for you.' Abruptly Marisa made for the door.

'You really should use some of it yourself. It might do a bit of good. You're getting terribly tanned.'

'Some people like it,' Marisa said bravely, and shut the door on her mother just at the right moment. It had always been the same right through her life. Her mother always succeeded in humiliating her somehow, even when she looked at her with an utter lack of interest.

Her father had loved her, but he hadn't been handsome and fearless like her mother. Her mother wasn't a creature of sweetness and light and she shouldn't expect it. Her mother was popular, wealthy and admired. After two years of incessant hard work she had a perfect right to expect to marry Tom. Marisa's own pinnacle of achievement was Cal McGovern, and at the thought of him the massive excitement he engendered in her made her close her eyes. She would rather see T.J. make the greatest mistake of his life and marry his young cousin than have Deborah compete in *her* world.

Either way Eve would tear the girl to ribbons, she reflected. Eve was really a creature of the jungle, and Marisa herself was caught in a web ...

Deborah's bedroom was on the first floor and adjoined a smaller room, furnished as a guest room, in which Christopher was now sleeping peacefully. It had been a long exhausting day and although Deborah was every bit as tired as her brother her mind and body refused to relax, without relief from the tension that had been her companion for many long months now. She shivered in the fragrant, flower-spiced heat, unable to break away from her morbid thoughts, although everything at Tom's was beautiful and welcoming. It was no use, however, to search through the large, lovely rooms for her mother. Her mother no longer had any place in this world.

Deborah found herself wishing very much for the impossible, knowing that she was a fool and had to make the best of life in Tom's tight circle. She had been left to comfort her young brother, but who was there to comfort her? She so desperately needed it. She had adored her mother, so warm and loving. Tom with his sensitivity had recognised her deep grief and loneliness, and his powerlessness to abate it; time would have to do that.

It had taken a good deal of firmness on Deborah's part to get him to leave the house tonight, but she had no intention of creating new problems for Tom. If his friend Eve Mangan wished to see him, and Deborah had been left in little doubt of that, then Tom had to go to her. They were very fortunate indeed in having his protection and support, but Deborah realised now that not everyone was going to show them the same deep compassion and generosity of spirit, let alone the same nice easy manners. She found herself remembering Marisa Mangan and the powerful core of hostility in her and she was dismayed. Sealed off as she was in her own numbed gravity, she still realised that she had already made a few deadly enemies. Not that they could really hurt her. Nothing could ever be as bad as losing her mother.

Through the opened doorway she could see her brother's sleeping face, half turned into the pillow. Poor little boy! She would need Tom to rear him and give him the care and firm attention he needed. She tiptoed to the door to savour the sight of him, the heavy fall of lashes on his clear olive skin, the handsome little face wiped clean of sorrow and discontent, A great love for him came over her, and astonishingly it eased the burden. She shut the door softly so as not to awaken him. She would have to remember to open it again when she turned out her own light in case he needed her during the night. This was a strange house and a strange environment.

Deborah couldn't help feeling proud of the way Chris was bearing up under his own grief. Their mother had made so much of him, indulging him and hugging him; spoiling him really, her only son. They had been such a small loving family, and though she tried hard not to start weeping, the ready tears sprang to Deborah's eyes.

She moved back blindly and hit her knee on a heavy piece of furniture, and the pain sobered her a little. Tom wanted her to redecorate the room to her own taste and make any changes at all she considered necessary to the house. Chris had already compiled a list of appropriate changes for his room and Tom was only too anxious to please them in every way possible: so anxious that it showed on his rugged dark face. Despite his size, his look of power and a certain toughness about him, Tom was really a very tender-hearted man, at least with those he loved, and somehow in a very short time Deborah had become aware that Tom was prepared and extraordinarily willing to love Beth's children almost as though they were his own. There was no way that this was possible in her own case, but Deborah had never learned to reckon with her own beauty and poetic femininity. It would take many months and heartache before she could finally accept this.

She sighed deeply and let her head go slack in her hands, and her beautiful hair fell about her, hiding her unhappy young face. Was there nothing that could deaden the pain? The life she had planned was nothing more now than a shattered dream. Would she ever get used to it? All families suffered bereavements. She had no right to forget her duty to her brother, yet it seemed humanly impossible to cut short her grief.

Lights swinging up the drive and striking her window claimed her attention. Could it be Tom, returning after a brief hour at the most? Deborah uncovered her face and stared at herself almost accusingly in the mirror for the tell-tale sign of tears. Her skin was very pale, but her dark green eyes were brilliant, evidently unchanged. That made her feel more composed. She pulled her soft silk robe about her too-slender, taut body and went downstairs to welcome Tom home again. He couldn't have cared much for the reunion party. Indeed it had seemed to Deborah that even if they hadn't been there to claim his attention, Tom had wanted his evening entirely to himself. He was too tired and slightly on edge, but from causes Deborah suspected were quite outside Christopher and herself. He had made two or three phone calls, one of which seemed to restore his good humour, then showered and changed. He had gone out shortly before eight.

While she was on her way down the curving staircase the front door chimes pealed out, low-pitched, mellow-toned but insistent. It was quite at variance with what she had been expecting. Tom wouldn't bother to ring; he had his own key, and in any case he wouldn't wish to disturb her. She hastened on down the stairs, obeying the obvious summons but despairing now because it might not be Tom. Her robe wrapped her slender figure quite adequately, clamped around her waist with a silken cord, but she wished now that she was fully dressed. The house in its bushland setting was fairly isolated, but the main entrance was protected by a colonnaded porch beyond with an elegant but highly functional security door and a series of ornamental grilled arches.

There was no need to switch on the exterior lights. Tom had left instructions to keep the house lit until he returned home. Deborah was praying silently now that it might be Tom. Coping with a visitor at this time of night and on her first evening would be beyond her. In the bright shower of light on the porch she could see a man standing outside the security door. She turned her startled eyes on him but he didn't allow her to speak before he introduced himself in a compelling, faintly derisive voice.

'Miss Nugent? Cal McGovern. I'm sorry to disturb you. Tom handed me over all the files I needed except one. I can hear your phone ringing—that's probably Tom now, trying to acquaint you with my imminent arrival. If you let me in, you can answer him. The matter is urgent, otherwise I shouldn't be bothering you.'

It was impossible not to believe or obey him. Indeed

it was the only wise course. She went forward with gliding, unconscious grace, sprang the lock and stood back while Cal McGovern pulled the heavy door outwards, then stepped in to join her. He didn't look at her immediately but refastened the catch, taking over the role of protector. She slipped a hand over her hair, a strange stillness fallen over her. This was the man who gave the O.K. on everything, and a little bubble of fear burst in her brain.

He was a man one would notice at once. An unbearable kind of man, his silvery, ironical eyes now slipping over her like some vast invasion of privacy. Her heart seemed to be beating with a heavy, painful rhythm. There seemed no way to combat his overpowering aura, no spell to chant, so she excused herself briefly and almost rushed back into the house to answer the ringing phone.

Tom's voice greeted her, comforting and definitely apologetic.

'Deb? Tom here. I hope I didn't disturb you, dear. I've only this minute been able to get on to you. The phone here has been tied up. Has Cal arrived yet?'

'This very minute,' she said quietly, conscious that Cal McGovern, a physically powerful man, very tall and lean, was standing just a few feet from her, silently studying her. She turned her back in a kind of blind protest, showing him her narrow, defenceless shoulders.

'I hope he didn't startle you? You sound a little tense.'

'No, Tom. I rather thought it was you.'

'I'll be home as soon as I can, but don't wait up for me, you need your rest. Perhaps an hour or so more. Listen, Deb, I'll have to be frank with you, I can't damned well remember where I left the file Cal's looking for.' He gave a short laugh as though annoyed with himself. 'Be a good girl and help him out, will you? It should be in the cabinet nearest my desk in the study.'

'How will I know which one to look for?'

'Cal knows. It's one of the green files under Ingram Consolidated. Just be there to help him out. Patience isn't one of Cal's great virtues, though he wants for precious little else. I can't think how it slipped my memory.'

'Blame me!' she suggested.

'Never! I'm more than happy with you. Be nice to Cal, Deb,' he said more seriously. 'He's very important to all of us.'

'I'll do that!' she answered, and hung up gently, not wanting to know Cal McGovern at all, much less be nice to him. Such force and vigour, and she had barely laid eyes on him, was hurting her physically. No one had a right to look so *alive*. It almost made her feel bitter, and that wasn't her nature at all.

Her face when she turned to him was impossibly remote, her green eyes brilliant but veiled. Wishing to be blind to him, she had never felt so overwhelmingly conscious of a man before in her life, nor experienced such a violent need to withdraw from any further contact.

'Tom was able to vouch for me, I hope?' he asked her sardonically as though *she* had no blind spots from him. His crisply curling hair was coal-black in the light, his eyes smiling faintly but not friendly.

'He said the file you're looking for is in his study. He said also I was to help you find it.'

'And you're prepared to do anything to please Tom?'

This was delivered gently, but somehow it stung Deborah like a slap in the face. Heat ran through her veins so that in front of his eyes she turned into a glowing, darkly red rose. 'That's exactly what I intend to do,' she said quietly, and walked away from him along the hallway and into the study, lifting her hand to the light switch at the precise moment that Cal McGovern chose to do the same thing and naturally succeeded. She withdrew her hand vehemently as though his touch alarmed and repelled her, and if her movement was pointed and telling she couldn't for the life of her have controlled it. The warm colour that tinted her pale cheeks bore witness to the fire within her.

'You're not very subtle, are you?' he taunted her. 'There's no mistaking your attitude.'

She chose to act as if she hadn't even heard him, and moved away to the big executive desk and put its bulk between them. 'I'm sorry, you were saying?' She lifted her head, watching his hooded eyes open fractionally wider. He had a hard, very high-mettled look about him. It was a tremendously individual kind of face; broad forehead, high cheekbones, shadowed hollows, an arrogant beak of a nose, an aggressive cleft chin and a wide curving mouth, well-shaped and full of temperament. Tom had asked her to be nice to him, but that would never be possible. His strange light eyes, as sharp and brilliant as diamonds, were trying to pierce her distant façade. His skin was burned by a tropical sun to a dark bronze. Many women would be fascinated by him, but Deborah felt only a remarkable resistance. Her own eyes were sparkling and the colour in her cheeks was lending her a false radiance. She decided that it was no time to keep silent.

'Please let me help you.' She meant to speak coldly, but it came out defensively. 'Tom said the cabinet nearest the desk.' She moved to it, anxious to find the missing file and have this man out of the house and hence out of her sight.

He gave a slight shrug and came round to join her, not attempting to touch the files but looking over her shoulder. 'Allow me on behalf of my grandfather and myself to offer you our most sincere sympathy,' he said, apparently with genuine consideration. 'I'm looking forward to meeting young Christopher. It will be a good life for him up here.'

'We had a good life where we were, Mr McGovern.'

'Don't hate me for it,' he said softly, and she spun around to face him as he leaned back negligently against the desk.

'What do you mean?'

'You've decided to hate me, haven't you?'

'I don't know you at all,' she said tightly and she hoped repressively.

'Your eyes are like mirrors and therefore revealing. May I call you Deborah? I can't go on calling you Miss Nugent. You're only a child.'

'I'm nineteen, nearly twenty. No child, Mr McGovern. But yes, you may call me Deborah if you wish.'

'I do wish. You should never show your feelings so clearly; that's why I say you're only a child. Here, let me do that. Your fingers are trembling. Are you sure they're not scorched?'

She made a conscious effort to placate him, knowing that her behaviour was unusual. 'I'm very tired. Perhaps it's that!'

'Then you admit it *is* something.'

His lean clever hands separated the files and selected the one that concerned him. He opened it up, let his eye range over the first page, then covered it up again, raising his eyes to look at Deborah as though she were a young person who vaguely maddened him.

'You're a very challenging sort of man, aren't you?' she asked.

'Oh, sure!' he said laconically. 'It helps in my line of business. Now you, Deborah, are a very sensitive girl. Too sensitive. Not everyone is going to comfort you like Tom.'

'Tom loves us already,' she said, encouraged by Tom's cherished feeling.

'I'm sure he does. A girl like you wouldn't be too difficult to love.'

Her heart was pounding and she could have cursed herself for it, because it made her seem so immature. 'You seem to be saying something I don't quite understand.'

'Of course you don't,' he agreed suavely. 'Tom told me everything about you except for one thing. You're too beautiful to fit comfortably anywhere.'

'Thank you. You're a very kind man.'

'Perhaps I'll never be kind. To *you*!'

'I won't allow anyone or anything to come so close to me,' she replied. 'I realise you're Tom's employer, Mr McGovern, so I can't really answer you as I might wish.'

His silvery grey gaze deflated her thoroughly. 'Don't let any concern for Tom stop you. He has a sure place for ever so far as I'm concerned. He's a good friend in a world where one doesn't have many real friends. I'd trust him with my life—but I don't think he realises what he's taken on.'

'I'm sure you'll tell him!' she cried almost bitterly.

'That's the trouble, little one. One can't really tell him.'

'You have the file,' she said, 'is there anything else you want?'

'I'm enjoying the conversation,' he answered smoothly.

'You surprise me.'

'I'm surprising myself, particularly when you're looking at me as though I'm the most frightening man you've ever met.'

She looked up at him, her dark green eyes eloquent. 'I think it gives you a sense of power to frighten people.'

'Silly child!' The amused, faintly cutting edge on his voice admonished her. 'Tom tells me you play the piano beautifully. You must visit us at Mandevilla. My grandfather has a passionate love of music and beautiful women.'

'And you?' She was challenging him, struggling with her dislike and fear, yet somehow it seemed deeply seductive.

'One, not the other!' he drawled. 'Actually I'm too damned busy for either.'

'You must keep it a secret.'

'Now what is that supposed to mean, Deborah of the emerald eyes?'

'Perhaps I thought you had time for one or two attachments.' The light fell downwards on her sumptuous hair and flashed out all the dark ruby tints.

He stared at her for a moment in silence, at the way she tilted her chin and moved at the same time imperceptibly away from him, her slender hand clinging nervously to the rolled silken collar of her robe. 'Shall we say I rarely meet with such fear and resistance? The ayes usually have it!'

He seemed to be blocking her exit to anywhere, his shoulders wide and rangy under the light summer jacket, a beautiful fabric, the colour plain in contrast to his silver and blue striped shirt that frosted his eyes and made them look that much more startling.

'Shall I ring and tell Tom you've found the file?'

'I shouldn't bother. Eve doesn't care for interruptions or competition. Of any kind.'

'I assure you she'll find herself without any. Chris and I don't intend to alter Tom's way of life. We won't interfere in any way.'

'That's very noble of you, Deborah, but then you have that look about you. Tell me, what do you intend to do with yourself?'

'I hadn't thought as yet,' she answered truthfully. 'My brother needs me just at the moment.'

'Of course. You obviously need to be cared for yourself. But in a little while, say by the end of the summer vacation, Christopher will be back at school.'

'I'll find something,' she said vaguely, afraid to let him see her expression.

'What have you been trained for?' he asked relentlessly.

'I've been junior music mistress at my old girls' school for just on a year now.'

'That doesn't sound very exciting,' he gibed.

'I wasn't looking for excitement, Mr McGovern.'

'I think it will find you.'

'I hope not.'

He said nothing for a moment, but when he spoke again his voice was kinder; a curiously attractive kind of voice, cutting and velvety at one and the same time. 'With a face like that you won't be very successful. You could make it your fortune.'

'I prefer to teach the piano. It's surprising how few people are really qualified to teach.'

'And you are?' His smile was faintly mocking, refusing to take her or her attitude seriously.

'I have a number of diplomas. I was conservatoire-trained.'

'Well, I don't know if that kind of thing is going to be open to you up here, Deborah. Kids these days want to be out of doors all the time, or kept busy with entertainments; they seem to lack the old application. If you're serious about getting a job I can help you easily enough.'

'I'll speak to Tom,' she murmured, deeply defensive.

'But Tom won't want you to get a job at all, and at your age you need to be out of the house meeting people, doing something. The money angle isn't important.'

'It mightn't be to you, Mr McGovern, but I fully intend to support myself,' she flashed.

'Which is exactly what I'm saying. When you feel like taking a job, I'll get you one. I'll find a good live-in housekeeper as well, maybe a married couple. The grounds need constant attention.'

'Why should you do that?' she said stiffly, hating his arrogance. 'Surely Tom can attend to it.'

'He may not think of it, my dear girl. Tom in some ways has retained an enviable innocence. He doesn't see people as they really are.'

'And you do?' Her soft young voice was full of scorn.

'I have the advantage there. Take care, Deborah,' he said simply, 'you have a disturbing effect upon me!'

'I find you equally upsetting.'

'Surely there's something significant there?'

'Nothing that I want to know about. I can't imagine why you're speaking to me the way you are. Surely you don't consider there's something not quite proper about my brother and me being here with Tom? He is our cousin, you know.'

'Yes, I do,' he said steadily. 'I understand he loved your mother passionately. He wanted to marry her. *She* was his cousin too!'

Despite herself Deborah's eyes filled with tears, panic signals flashing colour into her cheeks. 'You seem to be going out of your way to upset me—as though you've been waiting to do it!'

'How do you know you haven't upset me?'

'That possibility couldn't be in my hands, Mr McGovern.'

'I would love to tell you differently, Deborah, but I can't. Some women are born to arouse and make trouble. You're not what I hoped for at all. You have a power, or you will have, that can overturn the best-laid plans. It's a mercy you're only nineteen.'

'It hardly matters what age I am!' she said a little wildly, for her voice shook.

'I might have wished you nine.'

'I'm very grateful I'm not—I have to look after my brother. It can't make any difference at all to you. I intend to be a great help to Tom. There's a lot I can do for him and I want to repay him in every way I can. I can run his house, and quite efficiently.'

His hands firmly gripped the sides of the desk, as though he found the need to control himself. 'I'm wondering now what you'll propose to do next! It simply won't be necessary. Tom is a rich man. I think it's time now that he found himself a suitable live-in staff. If you want to make yourself charming and useful, arrange the flowers!'

For the first time in her life Deborah wanted to hit someone, to feel her hand catch the side of his face, to strike out at her enemy, but she understood that it wouldn't be possible for her ever to do it. Instead she shrank away from him because he was a little too close. 'You're a very arrogant man, Mr McGovern. Do you consider it your right to interfere in Tom's household?'

'I consider it my right to protect my friend,' he said curtly, his silver eyes a shimmer of light. 'Don't look so desperate, I'm not going to hurt you. Nor will I let you hurt Tom. Some things one can see all at once. Believe me, I know what I'm talking about.'

'Then you see things a whole lot faster than I do. You make me feel now that I should never have come here.'

'No,' he said softly, and bewilderingly his voice was gentle. 'I don't blame you or hold you responsible for being what you are. I understand your position, and your love and concern for your young brother. He does need you, and you will need him for a time. It's equally true both of you need protection. It was to Tom your mother gave her trust and she couldn't have given it to a better person, but she must also have realised that Tom is very much a part of the McGovern world: a closed world in its way. We all have to get on like one big happy family. What I'm suggesting is best for all of us, and you may rely on me to put it to Tom in the most intelligent way possible. You may think I have no place in your life, but I have, and you don't need to stiffen like that as if you'd break if I touched you. I won't do that, though you do have an out-of-reach look that would try any man's patience.'

For a moment she was totally absorbed in staring at him, as though she was failing completely to take in what he was saying. He had a ruthlessness about him that didn't diminish his terrible attraction, an attraction she might conceal for ever but never deny. Young and in-experienced as she was, gripped by sadness and uncertainty, she could still identify if not appreciate his powerful sensual appeal.

Marisa Mangan who loved him was welcome to such a man. He was a violent man, a man of strong passions under that enormous control. So engrossed was she that she was even unaware of their enforced intimacy, but he moved abruptly, his whole manner changing, clearly dismissive.

'I won't keep you any longer, Deborah, I can see how tired you are. When you've settled in, I'd like you to have dinner at the house. My grandfather is looking forward to meeting you.' He picked up the file and moved towards the study door, pausing for her to join him. The golden light shone through her hair and made her eyes blaze, but her face had paled to a delicate pallor. He could see now the soft shadows under her eyes, the tension in the too slender body. She was quite unconscious of her young, lonely beauty and its promise; so unconscious that Cal found himself thinking some kind of heartbreak was inevitable. He held open the door briskly, his dark face sombre, and Deborah found herself hurrying so as not to delay him. For an instant when the study light went out she fancied she saw a trace of anger there. She knew she should agree to visit Mandevilla, she knew it was important and she owed it to Tom, still she found herself protesting:

'It's very kind of you to invite me, but I have no wish to go out, you know. It's quite hard work just trying to be normal.'

'It's all arranged, Deborah,' he said as though there was nothing else to be said. 'I'll have the piano tuned for you. It's a Steinway grand. I'm sure you'll find it satisfactory.'

'But I'm not coming! I don't mean to be ungracious, but I'm not coming——' She stopped short because he turned to her and his glance made her tremble.

'You've begun a new life, and you'll do everything you're required to do.'

'You must know you can't dictate to me,' she gasped.

'Are you perfectly certain about that?' he asked quietly.

She closed her eyes, feeling drained and exhausted. 'After all, I'm not free.'

'I'm sorry, Deborah, but none of us is truly free. It will please me if you visit my home, it will please my grandfather, it will please Tom. It may even please you if you allow yourself to relax and don't go on insisting to yourself that I'm the devil just barely disguised.'

She thought he was demanding far too much of her, but she bowed her head as though crushed. Men ruled the world and this one was more ruthless than most. When she was stronger—and she suddenly hoped very much to be formidable and angry and shake this man— she would find a way to retain the pride and independence he was so contemptuous of. Little by little he had been humiliating her all the time they had been alone. Perhaps in a group he would be different, wear a different face for all occasions. He was not a man she could ever envisage loving, though why she should think of him in that way she didn't know.

'There's no need to come to the door,' he said sardonically, as she leaned rather wearily against the smooth polished banister of the staircase as though settled there. 'You're going to say goodnight, though, I hope.'

'Goodnight, Mr McGovern.'

'Do you think you could manage Cal?'

'No, I don't!' She was conscious of the tautness of his face and his shining eyes.

'You look ready to cry.'

'I never would while you're here.'

'We seem to have got off on the wrong foot,' he observed thoughtfully. 'I'm afraid it will be your disagreeable duty to snap the lock after me, since I can't do it myself.'

The short walk to the porch seemed to go on for ever. It was a beautiful night, the vast purplish-black dome of the sky thickly clustered with extraordinarily big and brilliant stars, a gentle wind through the great shade trees scattering blossom, stirring the senses with all the dazzling tropical scents of the garden. Beautiful showy orchids with golden-haloed throats stood in great planters, and sprays of the exotic native dendrobium fell in purple and pink cascades from hanging baskets.

Deborah stood silently beside him and took a deep breath of this strangely fragrant air so redolent of white ginger blossom and frangipani, the deliciously scented tuberoses and the six-foot banks of snowy white gardenias; an oasis of peace when no one could have missed the tension between them. The essential sweetness of her nature made her regret that this should be so, yet it was impossible to reach out to Cal. Such a man would destroy her.

'Goodnight, Deborah!' he said again, and waited for her to speak.

Her throat seemed constricted and he reached out rather abruptly and grasped her arm. 'Are you all right?'

She felt like a doll ready to fall against him. He had such power that one could readily hate him, yet draw on the excess tremendous vitality he had no use for. 'I told you, I'm a little tired.'

'Then I can expect you to be a little different next time I see you.'

'Only if I can expect the same of you. At least I'll be properly dressed. I should have apologised, but it slipped my mind.'

'There was no need, I assure you. Green silk plays a few

tricks of its own. Go inside, child, I can see the shadows under your eyes.'

She stod there a moment more, a little uncertainly, and he impatiently repeated what was obviously an order.

'Well, go on. Inside! Get a good night's sleep for God's sake.'

It was no use to look for kindness or friendship from him. She snapped the lock shut, her face appearing as palely luminous as a pearl in the shadows, then she turned away without a word, her head spinning. Briefly before she fell asleep she felt a curious restlessness in her that had never been there before. Next time she met him she wouldn't even flinch!

# CHAPTER FOUR

IT seemed extraordinary to Tom that the house that had once seemed so deserted should now seem so filled. He found himself returning to it each evening with anticipation and a keen sense of pleasure, for in little over a week it had suddenly become home. Young Chris always rushed out to meet him and hung on his hand, and inside Deborah and his newly-welcoming house was waiting. It gave him a feeling of such intense happiness and belonging that it spread right through his body and found itself reflected in his fine dark eyes. Man wasn't meant to live alone, and if Eve Mangan had done her very best to seduce him from the moment she met him, it became glaringly obvious that never in their best moments, and to be fair to Eve there had been many, had he felt a fraction of the peace and the gratitude that now spilled over him like a wash of light.

The house now was always filled with flowers, all the windows thrown open to the garden, and, because Deborah couldn't afford to allow herself to get out of practice—music. Such beautiful music as Tom had never heard in a very long time. The very first day after they arrived home, he had bought and had delivered an expensive Japanese grand piano, leaving the house that morning without telling Deborah his intentions and thus overriding any kind of protest. When he returned home that evening there had been tears and some laughter, and after dinner, a private recital.

Beth had played in just the same way, with her beauti-

61

ful fiery head bent over the keys, her expression intense, with surprising strength in the slender arms and narrow wrists. Having hungered for so long after such perfect company, a deep basic need seemed suddenly fulfilled in Tom. It was a sheer sense of decency and his own high principles that allowed him successfully to block from his mind the reason for his seemingly extravagant contentment. However clever he was at other things, Tom would never halfway admit that he was more than a little in love with Beth's daughter—or perhaps with the young Beth he saw in her, or a mixture of both, for he could never really separate them in his own mind. It was like some wonderful second encounter with one's young love, one's true love, with the exact quality of his feeling forever concealed.

Cal McGovern, with his sound common sense and consideration, had sent along a married couple for him to interview as live-in staff, and he had decided that he liked them and from all accounts they knew their jobs well. Within a few weeks he would have a section of the basement converted to a self-contained flat for them and it gave on to the rear garden. Cal had suggested, too, that in time Deborah might like to try her hand teaching the piano at the well-heeled St Mary's, but there was no hurry for that. Deborah looked after the three of them so well that it was like having a citadel against the world. He had more than enough money and there was so much for her to see. So much for her to do. The whole beautiful summer could slip away before Tom was prepared to think another thing about it. Time had finally stopped.

There was a measure of peace too, for Deborah. Chris had taken to his new surroundings like a duck to water, and if he suddenly came abruptly to a halt with his small face crumpling, the game over, there were many other moments when his laughter filled the garden. The pool was a favourite rendezvous and the physical exertion was proving therapeutic in many ways, for he fell into bed at night and slept dreamlessly, unlike his sister. In the tropical heat a pool was a necessity far more than a luxury, and Deborah's only worry was that he would get too much sun. With his dark colouring and clear olive skin he had already **acquired** a smooth golden tan, but Deborah, with the matt white skin that never freckled or took even the lightest tan, reserved her bathing for the early morning or the late afternoon.

It was very enjoyable and relaxing and it induced its own kind of peace. The huge free-form pool fitted into the garden and lawn beautifully with underwater lighting and a waterfall built into the pool so that the filter could re-circulate water over the flower-lined slate fall as well as through the return-to-pool line. A shady pergola, a barbecue, plenty of comfortable lounging furniture and umbrellas in the same blue and white as the mosaic tiles that lined the pool and the coping made it the ideal spot for outdoor entertaining and Tom had told her that he often gave a party there with Eve Mangan's help.

Mrs Mangan, tactfully, was giving the new arrivals a little time before calling on them. Deborah had spoken to her a number of times on the phone when Eve had called to speak to Tom, and she sounded a charming, self-assured woman with a rapid confident speaking voice and the ability to project herself right down the line. Her own attitudes were clearly the most sensible in the whole world and not to be ignored without some kind of disaster. She didn't seem the kind of woman to fill Tom with joy, but perhaps her powerful effect on the phone was no way to gauge the real woman. Like Mrs Mangan, Deborah would have to wait and reserve judgment.

When they went down to the pool late that afternoon, Chris ran wildly past her like a Red Indian, throwing his towel sideways, missing the table, then launched himself into the deep end. It didn't surprise her; it had been exactly the same yesterday. She never allowed him to swim unattended though he could swim like a fish, but unlike Chris, she felt water represented danger and accidents of all kinds could and did happen. He was her very special charge and she was the most conscientious sister in the world.

He surfaced exhilarated, shaking his head like a puppy with its ears wet. 'Beat you!'

It rang out like a loud challenge, so Deborah dropped her things and sprang on the diving board to amuse him, describing a neat arch into nine feet of sparkling blue water.

'That was horrible!' said Chris.

'I see. You can do better?'

'Of course I can. Stay there and watch me.'

'I'm not that crazy. Wait until I get down to the other end of the pool.'

'If you look at me,' Chris was saying seriously, 'I'll show you how to do it properly. Diving can be dangerous for girls.'

'Oh, rubbish!'

'It's much easier for boys. I'm doing you a real favour.'

'So you think I'm as bad as that?' she enquired.

'No, you're pretty good for a girl.'

'I might have expected worse!' she said wryly. 'You're so good that you're bound to make the swimming team in your new school.'

This, instead of pleasing him, made Chris scowl ferociously, something he did well. 'Don't talk about it.'

'What?'

'You know—school. I hate it. It's horrible. Year after year after year.'

'Forgive me,' she said politely. 'Are you going to dive or am I going to wait all day to perfect my belly-flop?'

'No, I'm happy to show you. Here, watch this. The starting position has to be just right!' Chris began to

64

demonstrate his idea of a model dive, which like everything he did in the way of athletics was extremely good for his age.

Deborah trod water and looked up at him, seeing his trim, well-knit little figure in his old school trunks. Whatever the struggles ahead, it would be all worth it. His skin had an even tan except for the white line around the top of his trunks and his thick dark hair clung in wet curls to his forehead. She felt a great wonder of love and responsibility, like a fight for survival. He executed a very professional looking dive, slicing the water cleanly and going deep, and when he surfaced again Deborah clapped her hands with real pleasure and no shade of resentment.

'You know something? That was very nearly perfect.'

'Yes, I know. Mr Frawley used to tell me I was first class.'

'Oh yes, Mr Frawley. He was quite an authority.'

'He just missed out on the Olympic team.'

'That's hardly surprising—he had to be forty. And you represent the future, little boy?'

'I'd like to think so,' he said proudly.

'So would I.'

'Isn't it beaut Tom having this pool?'

'Oh yes,' Deborah agreed, 'and you're conferring a great honour upon him by swimming in it!' She reached out and ducked him, and he swam adventurously underwater to the other end of the pool.

'Let's see if you can race me.'

'I'm not going to commit myself,' she said lazily, turning over and floating on her back. 'This is too lovely. A sapphire pool and the sun not so severe.'

'Come on, Deb, I want you to!'

She looked back across the glittering water. 'You think you can beat me in everything, but you can't! Not yet, anyway!'

'I did yesterday.'

She gave a hoot of laughter, her eyes gleaming. 'I didn't care yesterday—today I care. If I do have a criticism of you, young Christopher, it's your funny little killer instinct. I suppose all born athletes have it, the drive to win.'

'You'll see, I will!' Chris said confidently, his very confidence giving him an advantage.

Deborah swam slowly down to the shallow end of the pool and pulled herself up on to the coping, lining up beside her young brother. 'I've decided here and now, you poor little darling, that you could do with a setdown!'

Christopher licked his lips, his dark eyes already glittering with a sense of victory in hand. 'Who's calling?'

'I will.'

'You'll cheat.'

'What a rotten thing to say! I'm the elder. Shall we say the count of three . . .'

They hit the water together, Deborah's long slender body covering so much more of the distance. Even so she had her work cut out, for at twenty-five metres there seemed nothing she could do to prevent him from winning. She was tiring and it was obvious she was not really an athlete, but a stylish swimmer of no great stamina.

'I beat you! I beat you! Oh, I love it when I beat you!'

Her uplifted face was a little vague, a little hurt. 'Kindly concede a brilliant finish!'

'I had you licked at half way. You should get into training. Get into shape.'

'I'm in very nice shape, thank you.' Her face was rather pale from exertion and she was panting. 'Anyway, you can't play the piano.'

Chris chuckled. 'The piano! What a scream. That's girly-girly stuff!'

'The greatest pianists in the world are men. You know why?'

'Because they're stronger.'

'Yes,' she said, 'partly.'

'Well, I'm going to be a racing-car driver.'

'No, you're not!'

'Yes, I am, and I'm going to swim and play cricket and tennis as well.'

'That's more like it,' grinned Deborah. 'I wish you'd show the same interest in your studies.'

'Studies! Hell!' he said gently, and patted her shoulder. 'You're sure pretty, anyway. Poor old Nigel used to think you were the most beautiful girl in the world. Isn't that corny?'

'It's the truth. I *am* the most beautiful girl in the world.'

They both laughed and Deborah pulled herself out of the water, wringing her sopping wet hair. She hadn't worn a cap today because she intended to shampoo her hair anyway, and it fell in thick curl clusters that soon began to dry in the drowsy golden heat.

A voice called to them from the upstairs balcony and they both looked back towards the house in astonishment. Tom was never home before six and it was only four-thirty now. Chris jumped up full of excitement, and Deborah found herself rising more slowly because a tall unmistakable figure had come to join Tom on the balcony.

'Hi, there!' called Cal.

'Hello.' It was all she could manage against such goddamn charm.

'I liked your gallant effort, but really you were out-classed.'

'I always have been at any kind of sports,' she admitted.

'I think we can afford to ignore that!' he said suavely.

Tom laughed and looked over the balcony. 'Stay there, Deb, we'll come down to you. Cal has a surprise for young Chris!'

'Oh!'

'Well, your turn's next, Deborah,' Cal said. 'Don't sound so disappointed.'

She waited until Tom had disappeared before answering: 'You seem able to decide a lot quicker than I just how I'm feeling.'

'I know.' He kept looking at her and she was vaguely shocked. 'I thought green was your best colour, but now I'm not sure. Yellow is very becoming.'

'Whatever you say, Mr McGovern!' She was really annoyed now and she spoke a little heatedly.

'Don't let Tom hear you,' he begged her. 'He claims there couldn't be anyone sweeter or more winsome than you!'

'Please don't.'

'Why not?'

'You said you were going to be different next time.'

'While you, Deborah, have even less on. Don't be mad at me.'

'If you promise not to say any more,' she answered.

'You don't have to put up with my rudeness—tell me to go to hell.'

'I shouldn't worry about *that*!'

He laughed, and she could see the characteristic quick upthrust of his head like some high-strung thoroughbred. 'Don't run away. I don't want you to.'

'Really? I was just thinking I'd better keep as far away from you as possible.'

'Is there ever an end of a woman's hypocrisy?' he mocked.

'I certainly have no difficulty in telling the truth!'

He laughed again and moved away from the balcony with an exaggerated, elaborate salute, and Deborah hurried across the grass with a burst of energy she could well have done with in the pool. She ran the towel quickly over her drying body and reached for the thin Indian muslin dress she used as a slip-over.

Quick as she was, she still hadn't settled it over her head before all three of them came through the sliding glass doors that led out from the sun-room. At least the dress fell in a series of flounces to her ankles, a blend of rusts and browns and yellows, but of course it was sheer and one could see the brief yellow bikini beneath. From what little experience she had of Cal McGovern, she would do best to stay fully dressed all the time. She had a beautiful body, but she was extremely jealous of who looked at it and Cal McGovern's stares were altogether too long and level. She was sure he was doing it right now: staring.

To her great surprise, when she rounded on them he had his head turned away and was saying something to Chris, and the blood was pounding too loudly in her ears to hear. It should have made a difference to her feeling of agitation and resentment, but it didn't. She could see the way Chris's normally sober young face was lit up, and she felt too an odd stab of pain that he should have gone over so quickly to the enemy. Cal looked very smooth and sophisticated and he dressed beautifully; why shouldn't he? He had tons of money if nothing else. He lifted his head quickly and his searing light gaze neatly interpreted her sharp spurt of antagonism.

'Chris and I have just met,' he said quite pleasantly. 'I've been telling him about Harry Sommerville. He lives up here now in a kind of semi-retirement, but I'm sure he would be interested in a lad with Chris's potential.'

'That would be irresistible news to Chris,' she answered quietly, for Harry Sommerville had been a famous swimmer in his day and a better-known trainer.

'I'll say!' Chris seconded while Tom looked from Cal to Deborah sensing something different in the newly charged atmosphere.

'But you enjoy the pool too, don't you, Deb?'

'Yes, it's marvellous to be able to beat the heat. What's this surprise you were telling us about? It must be something to bring you home so early.'

'Oh, Cal and I were over this way, so we decided to come on home. If you care to walk across to the garage you'll be able to see why.'

'It's not a new car, is it?' Chris said, almost bursting with excitement.

'Now there's a thought!' Tom pondered. 'Deb will be needing one, of course. But no, son, it's not a new car. This is for you. I know you're mad to get your licence, but not for a while yet. I'm trying to save the surprise until the last minute, but it mightn't be easy.'

'What *is* it?'

'Ssh! You'll wake 'em up!' Tom silenced the boy.

'Of course!' Deborah said, and began smiling, forgetting in that moment that it was really Cal's surprise and not Tom's.

'There, Deborah, I knew you could do better!' Cal's soft voice mocked her. Neither of them was making an attempt to catch up with Tom and the forward-charging small boy. 'I wonder if it's really fair to have a smile like that?'

'Everyone has one.'

'Yours is the only one I've seen lately that might keep me awake.'

'You really should be married!' she retorted with a most uncharacteristic touch of acid.

He laughed, a deep sound in his throat. 'Good God! Why, deep down, Deborah, I'm a very shy person. Besides, why should I limit myself?'

'A lot of people prefer to be with only one person.' She blinked and refused to look at him.

'Don't delude yourself, child. That's pure fiction.'

'I don't think we were brought up in the same world.'

'For which I'm very grateful. I have to deal in facts.'

She shook her head—fretfully, wishing that she didn't have to deal with him. He was too magnetic and she was afraid of him.

'What very beautiful hair you have,' he said, 'though it's snaking funny little tendrils all over your face. You'll probably finish in a thousand knots by tonight.'

'I will if you stay on.'

'Well, really!' he clicked his tongue at her. 'Shall we go on and see the present? It's for you too in a way, but you're a big girl now.'

Deborah's hair did feel heavy and untidy, and the muslin dress clung to her, the spotlight of the sun directed on her young face showing a flawless pale complexion. '*Are* you going to stay?' she asked him.

'If you give me a good reason.'

'It would please Tom.'

'And never you, I suppose. I think you're trying to put me in my place.'

'Probably I see nothing wrong in it.'

'Ah, there you are, Deborah—you are!'

'It's a question of cause and effect,' she retorted. 'You, I suspect, are trying to bring me down as well.'

'It's fascinating, isn't it?' He glanced sideways at her and his silvery grey eyes were full of a kind of devilry that hurt.

Chris, inside the garage, was exclaiming loudly in a voice full of tenderness. 'Why, you lovely little things! Boy, this is a real surprise! Debby, where are you?'

'Coming!' She sprang away from Cal McGovern like a wary gazelle, disappearing into the cool shadowed arches of the garage. He followed her casually and saw two heads, one a dark glowing red, the other nearly as black as his own, bent over a basket containing two pedigree golden Labrador pups.

Deborah was frowning intently, her hands gentle as

71

she lifted one of the pups and put it into her brother's hands.

'Gosh, aren't they lovely?' Warm pleasure flooded Chris's dark eyes. 'Thank you, sir. You too, Uncle Tom. You won't have to remind me to look after them.'

'We got two so that they could keep one another company,' Tom explained. 'That way they won't cry so much. Cute little tinkers, aren't they? They're only seven weeks old.'

'They're wonderful!' Deborah said, and suddenly stood up. It was the perfect gift for a small boy, but it shouldn't have been Cal McGovern who had thought of it. Once she and her mother had discussed getting a pup for Chris; that wish had never been fulfilled. Her green eyes were burning, enormous with unshed tears. Tom and Chris, busily cuddling a pup each, didn't notice, but Cal McGovern's gaze was on her tense, overwrought young face. It was a matter of pride to her not to let him see how much this had hurt her. She stood swaying a little and his hand came down hard on her shoulder.

'I insist you walk to the car with me, Deborah. I can't stay, Tom, but I'm glad the pups were a success. Look after them, young fellow, and give them good names. Something I'll like the sound of.'

'You bet!' said Chris, struggling to his feet with the softly whimpering pup. 'Thank you once again.'

'It was a real pleasure, Chris. Stay here and get familiar with them. See you in the morning, Tom.'

'Yes, right, mate!' Tom lifted his head and smiled, and anyone who knew his face could see the change in it. He was alive and the gladness showered all over him, glossing his hair and his skin and his eyes. 'Hurry back, Deb,' he said blithely. 'It's strange, but I've never had a pup to care for in all my life. My old man was a tyrant in lots of ways. See what this little blighter is doing to my tie!'

72

'You're right, and it's an expensive one!' Deborah answered, making a supreme effort to join in the light-heartedness of the moment.

'Who cares? I'm having a good time!'

'Look, Uncle Tom!' Chris said delightedly. 'They're trying to play with each other. Put yours down on the ground and we'll see what they do.' He looked up at Cal McGovern and his dark eyes shone. 'They're full brothers, aren't they, Mr McGovern?'

'They are, and they appear to have found a very good home.'

'Little worry on that score!' beamed Tom. 'See Cal out to the car, Deb, then we'll think up some names. What about Bobby after you, Cal?'

'I've never been called Bobby in my life,' he protested.

'Your grandfather calls you Robert.'

'I don't think Robert is a suitable dog's name—what about Tommy?'

'Have a heart, I'd never know whether to answer or not.'

'What about Samson for this little fellow?' Chris suggested. 'He's very strong.'

'Samson had black hair. In any case we can't call the other one Delilah!'

'At this point, we'll go!'

While the puppies turned and twisted over each other and Tom and Chris were busy hunting up and rejecting names, Cal McGovern led Deborah out into the slant-ing sunshine. Neither of them spoke until they reached his car, but Deborah was conscious of that brilliant, critical gaze upon her. The car was the luxury status symbol she expected, when in fact he had bought it as much for its safety and high performance as its obvious attractions.

'I thought it might have been a happier occasion,' he observed dryly after his long scrutiny.

73

She gave an off-key little laugh. 'It certainly worked for Chris and Tom.'

'You know, you're a cruel little cat!'

'No.' She half lifted her hand to ward off the designation.

'Then you certainly know where to place your claws!'

'Truly, I didn't mean anything.' She dropped her hand and almost reverently touched the elegant front end of the car. She was acting deliberately to keep a control on herself, though where she had been very pale before the colour was now burning her skin. It was impossible to tell him about Beth and how they had planned to surprise Chris with a puppy of his own. The shock and the grief was all too near and it would betray her.

'You don't sleep well, do you?' he demanded.

'It would be a mercy if I could.'

'Then why don't you get something from a doctor?' he asked impatiently, angered by her stricken, exhausted look. 'We have any number who could help you. All good, capable men.'

'But they can't prevent anyone from dying, can they?' Despite her desperate desire to hold back, Deborah's voice broke and tears gushed into her eyes. 'Oh, go away!' she begged him. *Go away before you get through my defences.*

She might have spoken her thoughts aloud. 'And leave you when you're so obviously in need of comfort?'

'*You* can't!' she said brittlely.

'I could if I wanted to. I could even get you to come with me now.'

Some note in his voice, curt though it was, made her lift her head in confusion. 'My mother has been dead a few weeks,' she said wretchedly. 'Do you want me to laugh and sing and go out to parties? I'm in anguish, damn you!'

'Do you think I don't know that? But I can't think

74

why you're so anxious to damn me, and it *is* me, isn't it?'

She looked away from him, distressed because it was true in its way. 'It's illogical, I know, but you're so ...' She stopped in mid-sentence and bit her softly moulded underlip. 'I simply don't know what you are, or why you want to speak to me at all.'

'Probably that might alter in time, Deborah,' he said in a steely voice, 'but for now we all have to survive together and maintain the civilities. Your reaction isn't natural and I won't have it!'

She gave a funny little laugh, her burning eyes fixed on him. 'You speak like a man whose word is law. I suppose it's your position.'

'Stop that, right now!' Cal leaned forward and up-tilted her chin, not gently but forcing her to look back at him. She couldn't bear such a scrutiny so she closed her eyes, her thick heavy lashes touching the faint shadows. He still held her chin and his voice had an edge on it. 'If you're going to tear yourself to pieces, you'll be no good to yourself or your brother.'

'I've nothing to feel guilty about!' Her eyes flew open and she tried to twist her head aside, but his hard fingers still held her. 'I'm trying just as hard as I know how.'

'And you can't be left alone. These are the very times we need people. I don't mean to diminish your grief, you silly child, but other people have suffered and have been left to reconstruct their lives.'

'What I know and what I feel is too far apart!'

She spoke so sorrowfully that he dropped his hand, standing quite still just looking at her, his light, lancing gaze not ungentle. 'This weekend I want you to come to Mandevilla. Saturday or Sunday, whichever you prefer.'

She answered just as steadily and with extreme deliberation. 'I might have to come, but I won't want to.'

'No, you want to be lonely.'

'Yes, I do. Please listen. I can't—I *can't* go out!'

'But you see, Deborah, I'm going to make you,' he said softly.

'Why should you care?'

'It might seem cruel and impossible to you, but it's a simple act of friendship.'

'I'm not offering you mine.'

'Go on,' he said, 'you're determined not to spare me. Someone has to be punished for your desolation.' He was standing close to her and the whole set of his lean, powerful body seemed to brush her with danger. Through the pain in her throat she asked him:

'Are you inviting Tom too?'

'Indeed I am. Tom is changing right in front of our eyes!'

'In what way?' she was startled.

'All the evidence is there. Things you've never seen. In a very short time you seem to have brought a great happiness into his life, you and young Christopher.'

She was jolted into looking up at him and found him watching her closely. 'A man might have everything and still feel aimless on his own.'

'A man hungers after love and love has been denied him. I must tell you what you already know. Eve Mangan is expecting to be offered his name. They've been close friends for quite a few years now.'

For an instant their glances were locked and Deborah realised how formidable he was, the eyes and the mouth, the cleft, ruthless chin. She almost flinched for her resistance was fragile, and he seemed to be taunting her. 'If Tom wants to marry,' she said quietly, 'that's entirely his affair. But does he? Would a man wait for years to marry the woman he loved?'

'I wouldn't hunger after her a day, but I might have to!'

'You're utterly unlike Tom.'

'I'm afraid that's true. A lot depends on you, Deborah. You're not going to set yourself against Tom's marriage?'

'I would never harm him in any way.'

'That doesn't answer my question,' Cal said.

The instinctive reaction of her body was to tremble. She looked up at him, her hair drying into tight little curls all around her creamy oval face, her dark green eyes totally absorbed. 'You always seem to be telling me something you never get to the end of.'

'Perhaps you're only a charming, sad child. I'm wondering now if it mightn't be a good idea to invite Eve to the house as well. You can see for yourself then. You haven't met her as yet?'

'As you know everything, Mr McGovern, you must know I haven't.'

He ignored her little storm of antagonism. 'Would you have any objection to Eve? I'd prefer a quiet evening myself.'

'No, invite her by all means. Marisa as well. They tell me you and she are very good friends.'

'So we are. She knows how to behave, at any rate. I feel sorry for Marisa in lots of ways.'

'That's very touching. Anything else?' Then as the unconscious provocation of her voice struck her she put her hands to her temples, pressing them. 'No, don't tell me. I don't really want to know. I'm just making stupid conversation.'

'Yes, cruel and insulting!' he said abruptly. 'Why should you begin by detesting me?'

'I can't understand it either,' she cried.

There was an odd little twist to his mouth, an icy sheen to his eyes, but he answered mildly enough. 'It's a good thing for you that you look so exhausted, and since you are I won't retaliate. You won't always be safe, though. I'm sorry I had to think of the puppies just yet. It seemed a good idea at the time.'

He could see the sparkle of tears in her eyes, turning them to jewels. 'Do you know *everything*?'

'I understand you.'

'You couldn't!'

'Don't let it frighten you so much,' he soothed.

'It *does* frighten me. You know absolutely nothing about me.'

'It's a tragedy, I know, but I've been catching every nuance of your face and voice. I know you're in some kind of unbearable pain.'

There was no possible way to answer him. Deborah felt driven from his side and broke away like a punished child, threatened by his terrible perception. He stood where she had left him, looking after her. There was even a desperation in the way she ran, her thin dress fluttering around her legs, her rose-coloured hair spangled with light. He waited until she disappeared—into the house and not the garage to Tom—then he got into the long, powerful car and started it up.

It was something new for Cal to have a young girl look at him as if he was torturing her; it made him violent, but he controlled the emotion. Tom's feelings, that seemed to him so easy to identify, weren't anything incredible, and they could turn into another tragedy. Green eyes, brilliant outraged green eyes could break a man down. But there was no calculation in Deborah. She was too much of a child, and nearly prostrate under her grief. He suddenly realised he wanted it that way. For a time. When she came to life again that would be the danger.

# CHAPTER FIVE

MANDEVILLA took Deborah's breath away, so outstandingly had it been designed and furnished. It was a flame of a house, dazzling. But she made no fulsome comments, hoping to be overlooked at this elegant little dinner party. Robert McGovern had taken her on a tour of the house and grounds shortly after they arrived and she found him to be a splendid guide—a man quite out of the ordinary, but very, very kind. The grandfather of the man she thought she detested could reach her quite easily. She had started out with Robert like a grave, dignified young girl, a little unreachable, but he had captured her interest and made her enjoy his home and the extraordinarily beautiful things in it.

The grounds were magnificent, with peacocks in exquisite display and the much drabber hens strolling the thick, velvety lawns. There were massive shade trees, native and exotic, hung with great stag horns and with the giants of the fern world beneath their protection. There were large free-form beds of every conceivable flower in shades Deborah had never seen before, and a huge ornamental lake some three hundred yards long, in which floated black and white swans and the Blue Lotus nymphaea, the sacred flower of ancient Egypt. The conservatories were much further back through the trees, and there was an orchid house full of all the beautiful and showy flowers and bromeliads from all over the world.

Extensive as it all was, and far too much to be seen

79

that evening, Robert McGovern still knew every blade of grass, every tree, every flower; every stick of furniture, the best of the modern and the carefully selected antiques, the formidable collection of paintings, everything he held in trust for his greatest pride, his grandson. He made no attempt to hide this powerful love from anyone but began at the outset to point out all the things 'Robert' had suggested and even provided to make Mandevilla the showplace it was. 'He has the taste, you know!'

Deborah had smiled and inwardly concluded correctly that Cal McGovern had inherited his cultivated eye from his grandfather. A sense of unity had been maintained through the generations, and they were physically alike. Cal McGovern would be just such a handsome and striking old man, but Deborah doubted very much whether he would ever have his grandfather's gentle touch.

They had lingered in the beautiful brief twilight then explored the house, walking the long gallery that housed an important collection of modern art and then later, before dinner and the other guests were due to arrive, Robert McGovern asked her quite gently to play for him. Tom and Cal McGovern had by this time joined them. Tom wore his pride on his sleeve, because Deborah looked extraordinarily beautiful in a dress his money had been able to provide for her and because she was about to display the undeniable gift he thought of as an extension of Beth. Another man watched her too, his dark face inscrutable as she walked, a long-stemmed red rose, to the piano, without the slightest trace of hesitancy or nervousness, the faintest frown between her delicate arched brows.

It seemed to her she felt as strangely settled as she had in a long time and she contributed this to the distinguished old gentleman with his forceful, craggy handsomeness and his soft pronounced Scottish burr, who now gripped the silken sides of his armchair in pleasurable anticipation. It was a very big room and the acoustics were excellent, the lid of the Steinway having been raised. Deborah flung up her head, her hair that was darkly red in the shadows glittered into fiery life, then she brought down her strong slender hands in a Bach prelude.

It sent her back to her student days. All the hurry, the nervous excitement and the plans of the Conservatoire. So near yet so long ago—another lifetime. She loved Bach, the intellect and the purity. Bach healed. Then she moved on, both in her thoughts and her emotions. She played whatever came to her; Debussy and Chopin, some Bartók dances, a Liszt Consolation, the first movement of Beethoven's Apassionata. It was obvious that she would have been lost had anyone taken her music from her. She was a true musician with a maturity and technique that could take her far beyond drawing-room recitals. When she had finished and her hands dropped into her lap there was silence; a silence that seemed to be consistent with everyone's feelings. Then after a moment the old man spoke.

'That was wonderful, my dear. I'm truly moved.' She turned around on the long rosewood bench upholstered in an opulent flowering velvet, and smiled at him, such an illuminating sweet smile that Tom caught his breath audibly, remembering how he had sacrificed his own feelings and Beth's. It was impossible to look upon Deborah without thinking of her mother, and of course he remembered just such a smile. A swirl of love went through him, and at that moment his face was very revealing.

Cal McGovern looked carefully away from it, the aching longing, and he made his own voice and expression downright matter-of-fact. 'I should think you'd be wasted at St Mary's!'

81

'St Mary's? Good God!' his grandfather exploded as though thoroughly startled.

'She has to do something to fill in her time gracefully. I believe they maintain a very high standard.'

His grandfather continued to snort. 'Wouldn't you rather continue your training, my dear? Either here or abroad? You surely can't be thinking of teaching?'

'I had ambitions once,' she said lightly. 'I'm glad I was able to please you.'

'You have, my dear. More considerably than you know. Why, I sensed the moment I laid eyes on you you had untold depths. Such a gift shouldn't be shut away in a girls' school. Nor such a face!'

'Then why not consider King's?' Cal said in a breath. 'I'm sure there would be a world of profit there for the boys!'

His grandfather didn't bother to rebuke him, being so much struck by the idea that he laughed. 'What have you to say, Tom? You've been thinking pretty steadily.'

Deborah had gone to sit beside him on the long sofa and Tom turned to face her. 'Maybe it's true that Deb's gift is being wasted. I know musicians train intensively from childhood, but I would like to see her just sitting around for a while, enjoying herself. I want her to be young and carefree, and at least have the time to think what she really wants to be. I remember a quite famous concert pianist telling me once that life was hardly more than a series of empty hotel rooms, strange faces and countries with never the time for anything outside constant practice. When Deborah can give so much pleasure, and of course enjoy it herself, it might be enough. I wouldn't like to see her losing touch with the rest of the world. I don't want her plagued with endless hours of sheer hard work and then at the end of it to wonder what she'd got.'

'I don't think I have the dedication either, Tommy,'

she said softly, calling him for some reason she wasn't even aware of by the affectionate name of his childhood. A name that after he had left home not another soul called him by.

Tom found himself staring at her while both McGoverns looked at each other. Somehow she seemed effortlessly to have found the key to his heart. She had spoken to him as if he were a very dear older brother, so there was no reason why his hand should tremble, but it did. Both McGoverns seemed as though they wanted to conceal it, but after all it wasn't necessary, for in the very next breath Lee, the Chinese manservant, came through the impressively wide archway that separated the living room from the formal dining room to announce that Mrs Eve Mangan and her daughter had arrived.

All three men stood up, Deborah following, so they were all standing in the centre of the room when Eve Mangan swept in, a handsome regal woman with densely black hair and large dark eyes, her full mouth a rich mulberry red to match the colour of her gown. 'So there you are! How delightful to see you all. Mr McGovern, Cal, Tom! Deborah, how nice to meet you at last. I wouldn't have missed this opportunity for the world!'

Deborah went forward to accept the outstretched hand that flashed a fancy coloured diamond that attracted a good deal of the light. The older woman was smiling at her with vitality and charm as though their meeting were the nicest thing that had happened to her in a long time. 'Marisa, of course, you know. I hope you two girls are going to be great friends. Marisa?'

Marisa emerged from somewhere behind her mother, very eye-catching in a slither of candy-pink silk jersey with cross-over shoestring straps. She too gave Deborah a wide, purely superficial smile that displayed her small pretty teeth but never reached her moody eyes. 'Nice to see you again, Deborah!' Having been advised well in advance to keep the smile on her face she turned back to the men, saying something that made Tom give his deep, infectious laugh.

Conversation became general as pre-dinner drinks were served and Deborah sat back to observe Eve Mangan's gleaming, sophisticated elegance. She continued to effervesce freely with wit and considerable panache, a proud lift to her head, her full svelte figure dressed to perfection. Deborah felt that neither she nor Marisa could compete with this woman either in appearance or confidence, and she had absolutely no wish to. Mrs Mangan was a professional; a woman who held to the height of her desirability, a vision in the evening, for like most women she dearly loved the opportunity to dress up and Mandevilla was the ideal setting for a conscientious beauty, with tons of atmosphere and idyllic backgrounds.

Dinner gave them further cause for appreciation, with one delicious course served after the other to the accompaniment of fine wines. Deborah couldn't have asserted herself for the life of her, or fought for a place in the quick vital counterpoint of conversation, but her eye could behold the beauty of the room with its antique Spanish suite and magnificent console table, the paintings and tall mirrors, the Italian bronze sculptures, and the incredibly beautiful display of white orchids that had been brought in for the occasion.

As the talk rose and fell, she felt safely cocooned in her own little shell. Marisa's bright smiles were all being aimed to perfection at Cal McGovern, who sat at the opposite end of the long table to his grandfather like some medieval prince, very handsome, all-seeing and fiendishly clever, scrupulously looking after his guests while he noted Deborah's almost childlike preoccupation with the great drifts of sensuously beautiful white orchids. In her gossamer-light gown of lime chiffon she too had a dreamy sensuous beauty that commanded attention, but she was obviously unaware of it. It had exasperated him from the outset, though he had continued to speak gently to her from time to time; a major effort when he wanted very much to close his hands over her delicate shoulders and shake her into something like awareness of the situation growing around her. Eve's vitality and confident maturity should have drawn all eyes, but Deborah's dreaming absentmindedness was proving a thousand times more potent for poor lost Tom, who sat facing her and inevitably had to take the full force of her luminous and very youthful femininity.

For the first time in a long time Cal McGovern felt at a loss. Why should this child look like some impossible Renaissance vision instead of an ordinary, rather giggly teenager? It was unfair when he was so busy and overworked, though he didn't care a damn for that. Tom was his friend and this current situation had all the elements of melodrama. For more than two years now Eve had played a quiet, steady hand, and there wouldn't be much wrong with her as a wife for Tom. She genuinely cared about him. Perhaps he was the one person on earth outside herself she did care about, for Cal was under no illusions regarding Eve's maternal instincts. Tom, though very slow to form a permanent attachment, still had not shown the slightest interest in any other woman, so Eve had continued to dream her dreams. Deborah was different and she was undoubtedly a *femme fatale*, however innocent she might be. Already it had begun to worry him, for he knew Tom's face and his chasing expressions by heart. Tom was basically a romantic and if he was too old for it he was equally too old to be delivered a lecture. An act of generosity and compassion couldn't be allowed to go wrong.

Cal knew enough about Tom to recognise the signs, though the single upsetting element in Tom's feelings had probably not been allowed to reach his brain. Deborah's coming had made a formidable impact and he knew too that impression had found its way to Eve Mangan like an arrow. That dark gaze that flashed so warmly over their faces had been flawed the few telling times it had rested on a downbent, faintly mysterious young face. It was the very devil to feel useless and he was reacting with customary violence that never for a moment showed on the surface.

The glittering contemporary chandelier over their heads made of the table, with its silver and crystal and richly decorated china, an oasis of visual pleasure, but then too it seemed to penetrate every silken shaft of Deborah's head so that it was all light, springing back from her delicately tinted face and tumbling on to her bare shoulders.

Eve's clear voice stopped on a sentence, furiously aware that she had lost the flattering attention she was used to, following the direction of at least one pair of eyes. The old man too was staring, but she didn't care. Tom it was whom she could cheerfully have choked at that moment, and even considered it for an unbalanced moment. She thought she would never have to face any competition with Tom, yet here he was losing his grip over his silly little cousin, gazing at her as tenderly as if she were a flower. She didn't appreciate it, not in the least, yet she turned to the girl with a pregnant glance.

'My dear, what fabulous hair!' she said abruptly. 'I really do believe I've never seen such masses and masses. And such a lovely shade. Are those curls all your own?'

'You don't have to tell us, Deborah, if you don't want to!' Cal McGovern advised her.

She looked up rather pensively, but anchored by his silvery-grey eyes. 'I've always had more curls than Shirley Temple!'

'Exactly!' said Tom, looking puzzled. 'I should say that was perfectly obvious.'

'We were only teasing!' Cal smiled at him. 'I like them. In fact I find them much more exciting than little Shirley's in her heyday.'

'But then you do have an eye for pretty girls,' Eve put in swiftly and lifted her champagne glass.

'I do too!' Robert McGovern exclaimed, turning, smiling, to touch Deborah's fingers briefly with his extended hand.

They all laughed, but from then on Deborah was made to feel conscious of the rather unnerving glances both Eve and her daughter flickered in her direction. She refused another glass of wine because she wasn't used to it, and the lights blazed down on her lovely, composed young face, the infrequent but very sweet smiles. Her whole aura one of frail strength and a powerful capacity to arouse.

Marisa, suddenly glancing at Cal, felt the tight painful band around her head relax. For the merest fraction of an instant she had divined Cal's basic antagonism to T.J.'s ward. Her spirits soared and she rejected the fierce little jealous thrusts she considered might well have been turning her green. She had been right in assuming that the girl might represent a problem for Eve, but the fact was that at that very moment she didn't care. Cal was controlling some fast-running impatience. Of course being the man he was, so clever and successful, he would never be attracted to such a quiet, even aloof, personality. It was just plain logic. The vivid and vital sought similar qualities. As she thought this she suddenly relaxed, remembering her reputation for vivacity.

Coffee was served back in the living room, two members of the all-male Chinese-Malay staff, serving them silently and unobtrusively as they had done at dinner, adding to the general feeling of exotica. It was an enormous room by ordinary standards with high ceilings, but the furniture was all on the grand scale consistent with the comfort of two big men, and the large-scale entertainment that was a necessary part of their business and social obligations. It was all very seductive, the obvious wealth without the slightest over-decoration. All the beautiful, shimmering things in the room were balanced by something else, so that there was no feeling of a breathtaking opulence but an exquisite and very restful comfort and repose.

Eve sat beside Tom on one of the long sofas, greatly enhancing its solid dark golden colour with the vivid mulberry red of her dress. The French doors were all left open to the Mediterranean covered walkways that surrounded the residence, wafting in the balmy scented night air and the incomparable Queen of the Night growing in baskets around the base of the pillars that supported the huge central courtyard with its pool and stylised pool-painting in abstract swirls of aqua, a deep purple and green. It was impossible for the conversation to become private grouped as they were, which was why Eve much later announced that the Dawsons had driven them over—'they were passing the house!'—and she knew Tom wouldn't mind in the least driving them home. It all seemed happily settled, for Eve said lightly that she had one or two private matters she wanted to discuss with Tom, except Deborah was anxious to get home to Christopher. The arrangement had been for the sitter, a kindly middle-aged woman well known in the district, to leave at midnight, and very possibly before.

Her agitation must have shown in her eyes, because Cal McGovern immediately offered to drive her home whenever she wished. He understood perfectly that she wanted to check on her young brother. In fact he seemed *too* accommodating to Deborah's bemused mind. Neither he nor his grandfather had asked her to play again, and for that she was grateful, having judged correctly that neither Eve nor Marisa would take any particular pleasure in even a brilliant performance. She had created enough of an effect as it was.

When she took her leave of Robert McGovern, he had lifted her hand and barely brushed it with his lips, a courtly gesture he carried off with considerable aplomb and the confession that there was quite a bit of French blood in the family, which was perfectly true. Deborah was invited again, whenever she wished to come, and Eve, not to be outdone and partially mollified by Tom's presence and his hand on her arm, insisted that she have lunch at their home 'One day early in the week!' It could have been considered a very successful evening except for the undercurrents, but they were all determined not to show them, as if by ignoring them they would all go away.

For the first time Deborah found herself beside Cal McGovern in his high-powered, silent running car. He didn't seem inclined to talk but drove swiftly seemingly in an effort to cover the ten-kilometre drive in as short a time as possible. The light from the dash glowed on his dark, rugged profile, making it compelling and ruthless at one and the same time. Deborah settled down further in the deep bucket seat, so perfectly contoured, as though he might take it into his head to give her a violent heave out of the car at the very next curve. There was no mistaking his effect on her, like a blazing resistance to an outright take-over.

His voice, when he spoke, was so calm and so balanced in contrast to her own goaded feelings that she was almost ashamed that she had quite definitely passed sentence on him. 'What did you think of Eve?' he asked.

'A very elegant and formidable lady!' she answered.

'I'm glad you realised that. I was hoping you would.'

'What else were you hoping, Mr McGovern?'

'That you would enjoy yourself.' He glanced at her slowly. 'You didn't, did you?'

'On the contrary, Mandevilla is beautiful. I very much like your grandfather. He was extremely kind to me. The house is magnificent and I loved the peacocks on the lawn.'

'You wouldn't if you heard them at mating time. They're unbelievably noisy and the hens make frightful mothers.' He was reminded irresistibly of Eve who of course, despite her brilliance, made a pretty depressing kind of mother. She had been happy enough with Marisa tonight, seemingly finding satisfaction in all her bright chatter and her gleaming, well-presented appearance.

'I didn't know that,' Deborah was saying, visibly relaxing the tension that had been with her.

'They don't do it on purpose. It's their nature!' As it was Eve's. Women were charming and he was deeply glad he wasn't involved with any one of them.

'I don't think she liked me,' she said pensively.

'Perhaps not. Women are always feeling themselves threatened.'

'You're exaggerating. I don't feel in the least threatened.'

'Oh? Then why have you been nearly cringing in the seat?'

'You're assuming that. I was merely making myself comfortable.'

'Didn't they teach you at your convent that it's a sin to tell a lie?' he mocked.

'I daresay a confession would be very revealing, but you're not going to get one. Thank you for driving me home.'

'It was expected.'

'Not by Tom, I assure you.'

'I know that, Miss Green Eyes. Even in the dark they

glow like jewels! No, it was Eve who counted on my obliging. She's been attracted to Tom from their very first meeting, and she's determined to get him.'

'That's their business!' she said stiffly.

'So you can imagine she would be deeply resentful of anyone who tried to shut him out of her life.' Cal continued as though she hadn't spoken. 'Forgive my hammering away at this, but it seemed an appropriate time to mention it.'

'Why, particularly?'

'Why, indeed! You know, Deborah, it might be a good idea not to lose any time studying the people around you. You tend not to concern yourself with your surroundings.'

'I'm surprised you should say that. I saw Mandevilla very clearly.'

'Hold it! I'm talking about people.'

She shrugged. 'Well then, I saw that Eve Mangan and her daughter don't exactly relish my forced inclusion into the magic circle, though *Mrs* Mangan guarded her secret closely.'

'Did my grandfather make you feel an outsider?' he asked curtly.

'Forgive me, of course he didn't. Anyone else might require careful thought!'

He stared at her for a moment almost unbelievingly. 'It seems to me, Deborah, that you could do with a good slap.'

'That sounds ominous.'

'My hand must be cherishing the notion. It's tingling!'

'Very well! You're a bully and I'm immature.'

'I don't accept the first part, but I favour the last!' he snapped.

'Naturally, it's a crime to open fire on you.'

'Well, you were never neutral in the first place, were you?'

'No, I had advance information: If you like I can re-cite it by heart.'

'Do,' he said bluntly. 'That way you'll work it out of your system.'

'On second thoughts, I won't. They're all your friends.'

'Deborah,' he said in a clipped, decisive voice.

'All right!' she answered with controlled irony. 'Cal gives the O.K. on everything. Cal doesn't like stupid mistakes. Cal definitely isn't in favour of Tom's taking on a ready-made family.'

'Anything else?'

'That's about everything. So far.'

'I never said any of those things to anyone.'

'That's a bit hard to believe,' she said wryly, looking out at the flying miles.

'You have a peculiar idea of me.'

'Well, now, first impressions are best,' she returned.

'I think I'd better get you home,' he said vibrantly. 'You have a woman's capacity for driving the last word home.'

'I wonder you admit it,' she said with faint humour. 'I thought you were worrying that I was an absolute child.'

He half turned his head to glance at her and she caught the diamond-hard glitter of his eyes. 'Do you get like this after a few drinks?'

'I had exactly two glasses of wine. You'd really have to brace yourself had I had more.'

'I'm bracing myself now!' he said, his voice deepening. 'I think I prefer you beautiful with mystery, not these unnerving little outbursts.'

'The fact is, Mr McGovern, I'm not quiet at all. You simply don't know me.'

'Then there's a way to find out!'

'Not for *me*!' she cried suddenly as he pulled off the road and ran the car into a pocket of trees.

He switched off the engine and turned to her, and if his idea was to frighten her he was succeeding. 'You might use a little sense when you start out on all your taunts.'

'Don't you dare touch me!' she replied instantly.

'To hell with you Deborah!' he said softly, snaking his hand into her hair and giving it a gentle tug backwards. 'This is legitimate retaliation. Your face is like a flower, and unnecessarily pale. I'm not going to rape you.'

'I told you—*don't touch me!*'

'Who's to check up on us?'

'What is this,' she demanded, 'some kind of humiliation?'

'You're crazy, no one is going to injure you. I've had a half-formed desire to kiss you from the moment I laid eyes on you.'

'Then the feeling has all been on your side.'

'Yes, I know, and it grates.' Cal tilted her head back even further, a suspicion of laughter in his voice. 'You've only yourself to blame. It's terrible to be beautiful and a young girl.'

'You're hurting me!' she protested in the radiant darkness.

'Complaints, complaints! There's only one way to silence you.'

'If you do ... if you do ... I'll *kill* you!' she said finally.

'How sweet! I must say I admire your guts!'

'But you don't really *want* to.' She stared back at him, baffled.

'Certainly I do. Make the most of it, it won't happen again. You're right about one thing, I don't like stupid mistakes.'

'That's what I'm trying to tell you,' she said desperately, 'this *is* one!'

'I can hear you,' he mocked her. 'Such a martyred

little face, but it doesn't seem to matter. I don't know why. I am too, like my grandfather, a gentleman at heart.'

'You're a devil,' she said with intensity. 'And you have terrible manners.'

'It won't work,' he said, absorbed in curling her hair around his fingers. 'It isn't often I kiss a teenager and I don't need your permission.'

'You'd never get it!' she said, feeling distinctly odd.

'No?' For an instant his gaze held her shining, wide-open eyes, then his hand slipped down around her throat, making her feel strangely sad and lost though her eyes were sparkling. 'You have a strange way of showing it!'

'A woman of no importance,' she quoted sadly off-key. 'You're cruel!'

'Extremely, it seems to you, and I hardly know you. This may be very stupid of me, but I want it. Close your eyes, Deborah, and pledge yourself to absolute resistance!'

She kept them open with such intentness he smiled at her, his dark good-looking face touched with a certain tenderness.

'Let's get it over. I should like to know what your mouth feels like.'

Very deliberately but quite slowly Cal lowered his head and Deborah tried to catch her breath but could not. The scent of him came through the night air and her heart tumbled over and over, confounding her as she waited for the first touch of his mouth. It encompassed her own very lightly at first, without pressure, yet stirred her into great swirls of desire, the sensations so multiple, so tearing, so melting, that imperceptibly at first, her mouth began to open of its own accord. There was a static movement when his hard body tautened, then he swept her right into his arms, damning his own intention, cradling her slight yielding figure spread with warmth, and exploring her mouth in as near perfect a cascade of feeling as Deborah had ever experienced.

It was incredible, but every impassable barrier she had thrown up between them was instantly demolished. There was no sense or meaning to anything, but a powerful chemistry that triumphed where words would have failed. When he released her, she was trembling violently, and even his voice had a savage, improbable bitterness:

'You bloody fool,' he said very softly to himself. 'You could make love to her until the world spins off its axis!'

It was inexpressibly frightening, but she too was assailed by a hundred conflicting emotions. His very vitality, his driving masculinity, had given him the ascendancy. The desire to cross swords with him had only shown him the way to destroy her, for this was her great weakness. Inevitably in his arms it had been dazzling, urgent, unsatisfied. Her heart was racing under his hand, but he didn't shift it or even make an apology, shaping her delicate breast, claiming her by the very force of his dominant personality. He had kissed her deeply, bringing her to a precarious surrender, and she wanted much, much more, as though, knowing that breathless excitement, she despaired now that it had to stop. He belonged to himself, and here in his arms he seemed to possess her, bringing her quite literally across his knees.

How did it feel to be a clever man? Probably Cal had good reason to make love to her. What was disastrous folly on her part was his way of shattering for ever her blind spots. She had protested too much, like one of Shakespeare's heroines, when the taste of his mouth would linger on her own for days. Not even understanding her own warring compulsions, she struggled, and he held her.

'Don't go all melodramatic on me,' he advised. 'There's always the day of reckoning.'

'Would you please let me go back to my own seat?'

'I should, but you seem to fit every turn of my hand.'

'Don't,' Deborah said, with such a strange note of appeal that he half lifted her, smoothing back her heavy tumble of hair.

'You weren't prepared for it, were you?'

'No.'

'Sometimes one finds flashes of magic in the oddest places. Like under these bauhinia trees—they're supposed to ward off evil spirits, I believe.'

'They were deceived tonight!'

'I might easily have never let you go,' he pointed out.

'I'm glad you did. I want to be myself!'

'I could have sworn you wanted to be possessed.'

'No!' she said, too rapidly, afraid to look at him rather than the full moon that rode through the brilliant night. 'Can we go now?'

'Of course,' he said smoothly. 'At least you won't look at me again with that exquisite detachment.'

'I'm hoping to sustain it.'

'And it won't work. Perhaps both of us crashed!' He glanced at her averted profile, his voice mocking. 'You'll need to watch out, Deborah, from this moment on.'

'There's no room in my life for whatever it is you're suggesting!' she said emotionally.

'I can almost feel sorry for you,' he answered, wasting no time getting the car back on to the road. 'Are you trying to tell me that you regret it?'

'Of course I do! I'm not interested in crazy complications.'

'Then rest easy, little one. You'll have to beg me the next time.'

The heat that had swept through her skin still hadn't subsided. She asked rather plaintively could she have the window down and forgo the air-conditioning, and Cal simply touched a button, his silvery grey eyes faintly smiling, half ironic, hardly bothering to deplore anything. He had picked his role—and he was still concerned for Tom. They worked as a team, a damned fine one, and here was Deborah of the green eyes and the flame-coloured hair to act as a catalyst. He had to find precisely the most suitable person to look after her. It was that simple.

Tom wouldn't be the first man to go raving mad over a young girl, he thought. Any kind of climax had to be avoided and Tom's blossoming, easily-understandable emotions neatly sealed off. Eve truly cared for him and she wouldn't make a bad wife; Tom needed someone, the evidence was there before their eyes. Marriage would mellow Eve—perhaps for good. It was no secret that she had completely dominated her first husband. She would never do that to Tom. Maybe he didn't love her, but friendship was important and they had established a strong link over the years. For a man to fall in love with a girl young enough to be his daughter would tear him to pieces, and Cal had seen that kind of thing before.

He glanced sideways at Deborah, but she had her head inclined back against the seat, her eyes closed. He could see clearly the graceful line of her chin and throat, the softly moulded mouth, the small straight nose. An enchantress she might be, but it clearly petrified her. There was silence until he swung the car up the drive. He noted with approval that all the outside lamps had been left on, but still his expression remained fixed and very serious.

'Deborah?' he said to her as though she had fallen asleep. 'Come, I'll take you in.'

# CHAPTER SIX

JUST over a week later, Tom flew south on a business matter and Deborah began to be pestered by Eve Mangan. She had made one excuse after the other not to visit the Mangan home, but this time Eve was determined not to let her quarry back away. Her mind made up, impeccably groomed, Eve drove up the morning after Tom's departure, surprising Deborah before she had a chance to concoct any kind of story or even back the car out. Tom, with his phenomenal generosity, had already bought her a Triumph Stag; as much for her benefit, he said, as for Chris's thundering shouts of approval. Now both of them determined on seeing quite a bit of the countryside in Tom's absence.

Sliding sideways out of her seat, parked directly behind the Triumph where there was an empty bay, Eve quickly closed in on them as they sat idling in the garden, playing with the puppies and not exactly seeing eye to eye on which way to go, the river or the mountains. The senior McGovern had promised them that he would take them with him to Paradise for the Christmas vacation.

Paradise was the beautiful coral island off the Barrier Reef that McGovern time and money had turned into a luxury resort, a tropical playground for the rich and the holiday of a lifetime for the newly married, the fortune-hunters, and the comfortably retired. It was something to look forward to, but for now there were the rich fertile valleys to discover, the pineapple, the coconut and banana plantations, the never-ending fields of giant cane a rich emerald under a blinding blue sky. In these lands too, but further west, were the cattle stations, sheep to the south, gem fields for the tourists and the shuddery, fascinating crocodile farms, the McGovern tin mine and the silver and copper deposits that were being developed. There was so much to see, so much new every day, and they enjoyed their amiable bicker over which way to head when they were finally ready.

Eve's sudden appearance almost knocked them sideways. Chris frowned and Deborah got quickly to her feet, almost tripping over Wags, the more playful of the puppies. She bent down and lifted him, but he squirmed so much that she had to put him down again.

'Hello there!' Eve carolled.

'Damn!' Chris muttered man-like under his breath, but he scrambled to his feet, brushing little bits of the newly mown grass off his shorts.

'This is a surprise!' Deborah said pleasantly. 'May I introduce my young brother? Chris, this is Mrs Mangan, Uncle Tom's friend.'

'And your friend too, I hope. How are you, Christopher?'

'Very well, thank you.'

Eve regarded him keenly. 'You're not very much alike, are you?'

'We're a unit!' Chris said with a faint jar in his voice.

'How so?'

'Deb and I are a team. You mightn't think so, but some people only take two seconds to see a resemblance.'

'Well, I must be honest with you,' Eve opened her dark eyes wider, 'I can't see any!'

Deborah looked at her brother very quickly, denying him an answer, then back towards the house. 'Won't you come in?' she invited.

'Perhaps for an hour,' Eve said languidly, continuing

99

to stare at the boy as though he were an unpredictable element. 'So there are the puppies. They certainly look a handful!'

Chris's heavy lashes went down like fans, for which Deborah was grateful. It was true that they were very close, and Chris tended to be over-protective of his sister with an unchildlike and unusual capacity for picking up atmosphere and hidden meanings. Whoever he decided didn't like his sister had him to deal with. He bent down and picked up the pups, not enjoying this sudden change in plan or the slightest criticism of his beautiful golden darlings. 'No, Digby, you can't do that again. That's enough!'

'Well, well!' said Eve, thinking her own thoughts. 'Why don't you see what I've brought for you?' She turned to him but resisted patting the puppies' enquiring little heads. 'It's in the back seat of the car!'

'Really, what is it?'

'Go and see.'

Chris looked at her, then at his sister, and Eve broke in a shade impatiently. 'You like making things, don't you?'

'Yes, of course. But——'

'It's nothing! Just a game to keep you interested. Capsela, I think they call it.'

Deborah, struggling with her own feelings which ran along the 'beware the Greeks' lines, said very quietly: 'That's very kind of you, Mrs Mangan.'

'There now, I thought he'd like it!'

'It's very generous of you.'

Chris looked up at their visitor but didn't smile at her. 'I really enjoy making things. If you're sure you want to give it to me.'

'Would I have spent an hour trying to find the very thing to suit you?' Eve asked gaily, expecting a quick thaw.

'Well, thank you, very much. May I accept it, Debby?'

'Yes, of course.'

'I think I'll build something right now.'

'Good boy. We'll look forward to seeing the result. Oh, by the way, the batteries are in the glove box. I had to buy them separately.'

Chris walked towards the big Dodge and Deborah turned and smiled at the older woman, admiring her perfectly made up face and lovely outfit, casual but dressy. 'You've thought of everything!'

'Yes, I have!' Eve said sagely. 'Shall we go in, dear? I never like too much sun on my face. I'm afraid Marisa will look eighty when she's my age, with her constant tanning.'

'Well, she certainly looks very pretty now.'

'Well, of course, dear!' Eve suddenly laughed. 'You wouldn't expect me to have a plain daughter. Really, this is new, isn't it?' She stopped to examine a brass planter filled with cymbidiums in a beautiful scarlet-and-gold-speckled cream.

'Shades of Mandevilla!' Deborah said lightly. 'I thought we might bring in a few orchids of our own!'

'Careful you don't kill them!' Eve responded rather sternly.

'I don't think so. Mr McGovern thought they would do quite happily here. They need all the light they can get, but there's no full sun. I'm going to get some hanging baskets for all those beautiful butterfly orchids. It seems incredible to me, the splendour of the tropical flora—one would have to pay a fortune for this kind of thing, yet look at the size and number of the blooms.'

'I must be the exception,' smiled Eve. 'I don't really like orchids.'

'Oh? I think they're fascinating. Quite different and exotic. They use them a lot up at Mandevilla, don't they?'

'Yes, they have a fabulous collection, but they're mainly kept in the bush houses. It's quite a show place.

It had the whole State agog when it was being built. The architect lives in Manila—a brilliant man, and of course he knew how to design such a very large house for coolness. It's air-conditioned, as you know, but the *visual* effects! It's the perfect house for entertaining and they have a large staff. All-male, but then the old man's such a powerful personality, isn't he?'

Although Eve was smiling, Deborah divined some odd criticism. 'I liked him immensely!' she said. 'He's so vigorous and enthusiastic. One can easily see how he built up a business empire, yet he has time for people. He's really been very kind to us. He dropped in the other afternoon with Tommy. That's when I spoke to him about the orchids. He's quite an expert on them. Chris was nearly thrilled out of his mind because he invited us to Paradise for the Christmas break.'

'Why, how extraordinary!' Eve almost barked at her, leaving Deborah temporarily at a loss. 'I'm sure he's never done anything like that before. He guards his privacy like no one else I know, for all his entertaining. Paradise is the McGoverns' private retreat from the world.'

'You've seen it?' Deborah asked politely, leading the way into the living room.

'Many times!' Eve looked about her, up and down the walls and all over the furniture. 'My late husband and I used to stay on the island before it became the resort it is now. They were rather fond of Dennis for some reason that escapes me. The private residence is at the other end of the island. I've been there quite recently with Tom— it's Mandevilla on a much smaller scale and far less formal. Salt air can wreak havoc with the treasures!'

'I'm looking forward to seeing it,' said Deborah, waiting for the older woman to have done with her inspection and seat herself.

'Is Tom going?' Eve demanded, leaning back gracefully in an armchair.

Deborah halted as though she had only just thought about it. 'I think so. I mean I just assumed he'd be going. Now that you ask, I don't really know!'

'I sincerely hope not!' Eve said briskly. 'It wouldn't suit me at all.'

'Now that I think of it Chris and I wouldn't care to be away from Tommy at Christmas time. He's our family now.'

'Yes!' Eve drew the word out. 'That Stag must have set him back ten thousand dollars or so.'

'I didn't ask for it!' said Deborah, colouring faintly under that accusing dark stare.

'No, dear, I didn't say you did. The piano now, did you ask for that?'

'It does something for the room, don't you think?' parried Deborah. 'Tom loves music.'

'Then he's kept it very dark until now!'

Eve's earlier mood of affability seemed to be deteriorating under waves of jealousy. 'Won't you let me get you something?' Deborah asked, and stood up resolutely.

'Tea. Lemon tea,' Eve said, exactly as if she were at a board meeting. 'Nothing with it.'

*Thank you!* Deborah finished wryly to herself.

'You go and make it and I'll just wander around here. You seem to have made quite a few changes in a short space of time.'

'I hope you like them!' Deborah looked back over her shoulder.

'You have taste—perhaps not that particular painting in here. What's it supposed to be anyway?'

'*Hymn to the Sun*. I think it's beautiful and it's quite valuable. Prices for modern Australian art are soaring.'

'You seem very knowledgable,' Eve said, and Deborah smiled.

'I had a friend whose grandfather had an extensive collection. He gave it to the University just recently.

Anne and I visited a lot, and we became quite familiar with all the leading artists' work. Professor Connaught was a wonderful man, and he always went out of his way to cultivate our interest and awareness. I don't think Tom knew what he had here. He bought it a few years ago when a friend dragged him along to a private showing.'

'I've never seen it.'

'No, it's never been hung. Tom said he didn't know the best place to put it.'

'I don't think you've found it now. One wonders what else you'll turn up.'

'Excuse me for a moment. I'll get your tea.'

In the kitchen Deborah put the water to boil and set out the things in a curiously absorbed way, then when they were perfectly in order she set out the tray. The water boiled, the tea was made. Where did she go from here? Eve Mangan she knew for an enemy. It had been in her subconscious mind all along. Perhaps she had come here to smash her. She looked a very strong woman, a law unto herself, and she was indisputably hostile. The tray looked inviting, the lace mat, the delicate china, the silver tea pot and the sugar bowl, though Deborah had the dismal feeling that Mrs Mangan wouldn't take to any kind of sweetness. When she had left her roaming around the living room she had a decidedly hard and resolute air about her, as though having thought up a campaign she was about to mount it.

Another ten minutes passed in which Eve drank her tea as if she genuinely needed it, then she set down her cup in its fragile decorated saucer and launched into the matters about which she had really come. 'You're an intelligent girl, Deborah,' she began fairly, 'and as you say you've become part of Tom's family.' She broke off, her dark eyes enquiring. 'You don't mind if I speak freely?'

It would be hard indeed to stop you, Deborah thought

wryly, but she made a graceful gesture of encouragement with her right hand.

'You know of course that Tom and I plan to marry?'

'Well,' Deborah said as a counter measure, 'he hasn't spoken to me of his private affairs, Mrs Mangan.'

'Eve, please. I prefer to be called by my christian name.'

'Thank you, but as I told you, Tom hasn't discussed his private affairs with me and I wouldn't expect him to.'

'You're right, of course,' agreed Eve. 'You couldn't expect him to accept you fully into his confidence. It's quite true, but it was rather a setback for us your mother dying.'

'It was a tragedy for my brother and me.'

'Yes, I know, forgive me!' Eve said quickly. 'How could I have been so unthinking? What I'm trying to say, my dear, is that Tom is rather a noble character in this jungle world of ours. He's been caught into a certain commitment that I for one wouldn't dream of interfering in; I only hope you realise how hard it is on me. I know I look a young woman, but I'm not. Let's face it, I'll never see forty again. I'm at the stage in my life when I want to be settled. Do I have your attention?'

'Quite. I understand that you want to be settled, and that Tommy is a fine man.'

'What's this *Tommy*?' Eve asked with a flash of real irritation. 'It falls oddly on the ear.'

'Not on mine,' countered Deborah.

'Precisely. Young people are good on nicknames and so forth. Had it not been for you and your brother, I daresay Tom and I would be busy making plans now.'

Deborah pondered this a moment and her voice was quite gentle. 'Don't let us stop you. We can only live each day as it comes, Mrs Mangan. If and when Tommy marries the whole situation will change.'

'I should hope so.' Eve stared at her intensely. 'I must say I resent your choice of words, *if and when*. Tom is going to marry me, be in no doubt of it. Everyone is expecting it, and believe me, it has the McGovern sanction.'

'I never take sides myself, though I imagine that's tantamount to a heavenly blessing,' Deborah said dryly. 'All Tommy has to do is tell us. It's his life and I can't foresee any real difficulty. We wouldn't dream of interfering.'

'But you have done so already, haven't you? Why, you've even turned this room around so I hardly recognise it. Tom had an excellent decorator, one of my closest friends.'

'I'm sorry I've angered you. I realise it was handled by a professional. I've made very few changes really, and Tommy seems to like them.'

Eve deliberately crushed a flower head. 'Would you please stop that ridiculous name? Call him Tom or T.J. if you prefer.'

'Allow me to make up my own mind about that!' Deborah said somewhat more crisply. 'What is it exactly you want of me?'

'Make it easy for Tom,' Eve responded coldly. 'Men are actually no good at running their lives. I'm not asking you to move out immediately, nothing like that. I'm not one to see two orphans suffer. But you're an intelligent girl—Tom tells me you play the piano extremely well. I'm sure you'll find a teaching position. The convent schools seem to go in for that kind of thing, if you can stand the nuns. When the holidays are over young Christopher will be going to school. Have you thought of a good boarding school?'

'I would *never* think of a boarding school!' Deborah interposed flatly. 'We've just lost our mother and Chris needs much love and reassurance. He needs me and now he needs Tommy, for we've both come to love him. He's exactly how my mother described him.'

Eve gave a tight, ugly laugh, a glitter of evil amusement in her lustrous eyes. 'It's a mistake to fool yourself, young lady!'

'I beg your pardon?'

Eve contemplated the astounded young face before her, the upthrust of the small proud head with its gleaming romantic curls. 'Perhaps you *are* a fool,' she said grimly. 'Tom is a very attractive man. Many women think so. It's absurd for you to be talking about loving him as though he was a dear doddery old uncle.'

'No, an older brother!' Deborah said protectively. 'I think of him very easily in that way.'

'And how does he think of you, a young sister? I don't think so, but then I was never a fool.'

'Please!' Deborah shook her head, a spasm of distaste passing across her face. 'Pursuing that line of talk would be in extremely poor taste.'

'Oh, really?' Eve mocked her, swinging one shapely leg. 'Tom, my dear, is a *man,* and I would advise you to watch your step!'

Deborah's eyes glowed greenly in her whitening face. 'I don't understand you. I don't understand how you can talk about loving, then say a thing like that. Tommy is above anything like that. He sets a very high standard of behaviour—I have nothing but a deep affection and respect for him. He's brought a great kindness and healing into our lives and I intend to make up for it.'

'How? By remaining in his house?' Eve suddenly glared at her.

'Certainly, until he's married, but are you certain he wants to marry? He doesn't speak as if he had any immediate plans.'

Eve made a sudden movement as if she wanted to attack her. 'Because, of course, you've thwarted them! You can see, can't you, that he's saddled himself with a ready-made family? Why, if you had any self-respect you'd find yourself a job. Get out and look after your brother.'

'I'll do that when Mr and Mrs Ryan settle in, but until then I believe I'm performing a useful service in running this house. Tommy has had no complaints. He looks well and happy.'

Eve by now was almost beside herself, her contralto, rather actressy voice vicious. 'There are a devil of a lot of people who are worried about this situation.'

'What situation? Situations are more often caused from without than within.'

'Then answer me this—a truthful answer if you don't mind. Do you want to see Tom married to me?'

'I want what Tommy wants,' Deborah sidestepped neatly.

'Which is not answering my question.'

'You can't expect me to see you as Tommy does.'

'Then I take it you're dead set on destroying my chances?'

'I don't think I can bear any more of this!' Deborah said suddenly. 'What chances are you speaking of, Mrs Mangan? You've told me you've gone far beyond the chances stage. If Tommy wants to marry you, that's hardly within my control. I only want him to be happy. I don't think he's been truly happy, and he deserves to be.'

'You're speaking as a woman, of course,' Eve sneered at her, 'not a little sister.'

'Dear God!' Deborah said it in a whisper. 'There's no man–woman relationship between us, nor will there ever be. Tommy is family. You insult us both by suggesting any other thing. Now I must ask you to go. We're only having a bad effect on one another.'

'And it could easily get worse. I came to you in confidence to ask you to help me, instead you've been most impertinent and obstructive. It was a mistake, I see that now. A bitter mistake, but I've learnt from it. I'll wipe you out, but first I'll grant you this summer holiday, Miss Nugent. After that, see how you go!' She stood up, looking what she was, a rich, forceful woman and an undeniable enemy.

'Mrs Mangan, you're overwhelming me with your hostility,' Deborah said quietly. 'It's so unjustified, and I hope you see that when you're feeling a little cooler. You must know we came to this house knowing very little of Tommy's background. I had no knowledge of you or a pending marriage when he invited us. It seemed as though he really wanted us . . .'

'He was blackmailed, you mean!' Eve shouted, her full mouth a thin line. 'Men have been from time immemorial.'

Deborah was beginning to feel ragged and was driven to protest: 'Why are you talking like this? It's so ugly. Tommy loved my mother, did you know that?'

'What, twenty years ago? Calf love. He didn't marry her, did he?'

'He wasn't allowed to. Neither of them were old enough or secure enough to go against both families' wishes. They were first cousins.'

'Please!' Eve waved a jewelled hand, less lovely than the rest of her person. 'Spare me this nauseating tale.'

'You can't ignore it,' Deborah said gravely, 'that abiding love is the reason why we're here. I think Tommy even feels he has been rewarded in some way. He can't do enough for us, and he seems so happy.'

'It's a high price to pay for this sickly happiness, and it's unhealthy!'

Deborah's young face was a study in pain. 'You appal me, Mrs Mangan, and I'm quite sure you'd disgust Tommy.'

'Why, you cheeky little upstart!' Eve cried, exasperated, swinging closer to the standing girl. 'Don't *you* try to tell me about Tom. I've shared more than two years of my life with him—and my bed. Now I want marriage.'

'If he loves you that's what you'll get. We can always change our plans. Just knowing that Tommy was somewhere there would be enough. Chris needs a man's hand and influence.'

'Yes, I can see that. I wasn't at all enchanted. It might be an idea if you started looking for a man of your own.'

'A woman's life can be successful without one,' Deborah said serenely. 'I won't be twenty until the New Year. I think I have time.'

'Well, *I* haven't!' Eve burst out bitterly. 'Don't think you're going to waste my ambitions. Tom and I share a tender, honest relationship. He has become my whole existence and I'll be good to him. Before you and your brother came on the scene I had the sure knowledge that we would marry.'

'Then nothing has altered. Can't you be a little more generous, Mrs Mangan? We've been here such a short time. Do you begrudge us even that? Not so long ago we lost the most important person in our lives. You're not the only person who had plans, but you're lucky to be alive to make them.'

Eve gave a thin little laugh. 'I don't imagine for one moment that you could have managed anything like this. Neither would you have ever rated an invitation to Mandevilla, let alone the island. Incidentally, you have no prospects there—I'm very ambitious for my daughter. I've put a lot of time into her and I intend to be rewarded. You must be perfectly well aware that Cal is far from indifferent to her. You see, you don't fit into our little niche!'

'And I'm not wasting time feeling sorry for myself. What I am sorry about is that you should put into words things that should never have been spoken.'

'You're no judge of that,' Eve said contemptuously,

'and you can't lie to me. Men in their forties marry girls like you, for example, every day. And tire of them.'

'You're not very loyal to Tommy,' Deborah said gently.

'Tom's a fool. It's true enough. He's quite capable of falling in love with you. Haven't you seen his eyes? He's a romantic!'

'You'll have to try much harder to convince me of that,' Deborah said a little shakenly. 'He did love my mother. Perhaps he sees a little of her in me.'

'How maudlin! But I suppose it does happen. That fact doesn't seem to be troubling you.'

'I find it unbelievable. You don't know Tommy at all!'

'No?' Eve gave a dark laugh. 'You tell me. You haven't a thought in your curly head. Let me give you some advice, Miss Purity, get out and meet some young men. Leave my man alone. Don't ever give him an opportunity to consider you in that light. You can be sensible about this!'

Deborah brought her green eyes to bear on the other woman, hard and contemptuous. 'What you're saying is outrageous and I won't listen. I'm not pretending, either, that I admire you for it. You're supposed to love Tommy, yet you can stand there and say such things about him!'

'How boring are the young!' gibed Eve. 'It really is a crime to be such a silly little ostrich. Let me put it plainly: I want Tom and I intend to get him. I've sacrificed more than two years of my life, years I couldn't afford to waste. The irreplacable years. You'll know soon enough what it feels like to be ageing. A woman loses her desirability fast. Tom and I are lovers and I need him. It's as simple as that!' She said it proudly and emphatically because it was true.

Suddenly Deborah felt sorry for her, for she and Chris had presented her with a dilemma. 'All I want is to live pleasantly with all Tommy's friends, and naturally that includes you, Mrs Mangan. What you're saying is cruel, and in saying it I think you lose some of your dignity. I quite genuinely wish that everything might be different between us, but of course that's not possible now. I can only tell you that I wouldn't dream of repeating a word of this to anyone.'

'It would do you no good!' Eve answered shortly. 'I positively have the strength on my side. Live every day as best you can, but when the end of the holidays come ...'

'This isn't getting us anywhere!' Deborah shook her head.

'You've got a lot to learn.'

'You're right. Now I'd like to get started on some picnic arrangements I made with Chris. I'll come with you to the door.'

'Do that!' Eve said, and laughed harshly. 'It will be an extremely short time that *you'll* be running this house!'

Christopher, coming in to show his first rather spectacular effort, caught these words and the passionate malice behind them. His handsome little face went blank and his eyes filmed over.

'You're just like the other one, aren't you?' he asked.

'Have a care how you speak to me, sonny!' Eve thundered from the depths of her terrible vanity.

'And you watch how you speak to my sister otherwise you'll have someone else to deal with—that's me.' Chris scowled. 'I'm not scared of you. Here, take the Capsela— I don't want it and you didn't really want to give it to me. I should have known—I *did* know. I'll get the rest of it and put it in your car. She's leaving now, isn't she, Debby?'

'Please, Chris!' Deborah gave him a rebuking look. 'Go quietly and get the rest of the set. Mrs Mangan is Uncle Tom's friend. He would expect us to be polite to her!'

'And he'd expect her to be polite to us. Why have kids

always got to be the polite ones? *Why* don't you like us?' he demanded of the stony-faced Eve. 'We haven't done anything to you. Why do you speak to Debby like that, as if you hate her? No one hates Debby.'

Eve's dark eyes glittered with distaste, and she glanced with disparagement at the silent girl. 'It will be a miracle if you rear this boy without a parcel of trouble. He's a little hooligan!'

'No! He's too alert and his intuitions are too sharp, but he's generally very well-mannered. Children aren't fools, you know. The male usually protects the female!'

Eve, seized by an impulse, laughed aloud. 'I imagine he'll have a real story to tell Tom.'

'He won't be saying anything,' Deborah said sharply, 'and I would advise you not to attack him. Chris, go and get that set immediately!'

'Yes, Deb.'

'Altogether a lovely little family!' Eve drawled as she picked up her things. 'I'll make my farewell, my dear. Thank you for the tea. Remember what I said.'

'And I don't believe a word of it!' Deborah told her quietly.

'You'll see!' Eve walked confidently to the door, as regal as a queen. 'There now, your sweet little brother is returning my gift. I hope he hasn't broken anything so I can return it to the shop. He looks a destructive child to me.'

Deborah's heavy lashes fluttered, but she kept her voice even. 'You should be honest with children, Mrs Mangan. They're never fooled for very long.'

Eve's sardonic face wore an insulting expression. She swept Deborah up and down in a mocking appraisal, then she looked back at the child. 'I thought you were bad enough, but I see now that he'll be my biggest problem. Your mother obviously ruined him. He appears to have learnt nothing in the way of manners.'

'*You* don't appear to find them worth bothering about.'

For an instant Eve's carefully tended jawline knotted. 'That really should earn you a smack in the face!'

'I'm glad you've decided not to,' Deborah said dryly. 'It would be extremely interesting to see what Chris would do. He's not backward in galloping into the attack!'

Eve raised her dark eyebrows, plucked to a fine arch. 'Tom must be going soft in his old age to assume responsibility for such an undesirable child.'

'Perhaps it's as hard for us to believe he cares about you,' Deborah broke in simply and without emotion. 'Now I'm going to call Chris and I'm going to shut the door. Goodbye, Mrs Mangan. I regret our entire conversation.'

'You'll have good reason to. Goodbye, my dear!' she said graciously as she moved down the terraced stairs. 'I have a press of invitations, so I must fly. Goodbye, little boy,' she called unpleasantly to Chris. 'Hurry up to your sister now. You wouldn't want anything bad to happen to her!'

'If it did, I'd think of something to hurt *you!*' he hurled at her fiercely.

For the first time Eve looked positively startled. She approached her car at a rush, as if such a belligerent, undisciplined child might well take it into his head to turn the sprinkler on her.

It had struck Chris's mind to do it, but he rejected the notion, knowing full well that his sister was quite capable of giving him a hard slap. He ran up the steps to her and her hand fell protectively over his shoulder. 'Good riddance, you old bitch!' he hissed bleakly.

'I've told you and told you, Chris, not to swear.'

'Bitch isn't swearing. Everyone swears these days. We sure didn't win any popularity poll there! What was the matter with her, what was she going on about? You should have seen her face. It was horrible.'

'Undoubtedly she doesn't like us!'

Hand in hand they watched Eve nearly put the Dodge into a spin on the gravel, then she regained control and swept down the drive, braking furiously just before the road. 'I'm just glad I was about to rescue you!' said Chris.

'Thank you, darling, I know you'd do anything for me. We won't say anything to Tommy or anyone else, understand?'

'Why not?' He snapped off to look up at her. 'You can bet *she'll* go on and on to anyone who'll listen!'

'I don't think she will, and we won't either,' Deborah said quietly. 'We've got to remember they're all very close up here, and we're the outsiders. Just because she doesn't like us it doesn't mean she doesn't care about Tommy. She told me she loves him.'

'Yuck!' Chris exclaimed in astonishment. 'You mean they're going to get married? In a church?'

'I don't know about the church, but yes, they may get married.'

'Then we'll know what to do. You won't have to wait long for me to leave school. Maybe when I'm fourteen. I hate it anyway. I'll get a job. I'll help you just as soon as I can!'

'You're the best brother in the world!' Deborah said softly.

'Mum said I had to look after you *always*!' Tears rushed into his eyes and he blinked them back fiercely. 'Are we still going on our picnic?'

'Why not?' Deborah surrendered her own wave of sadness and spoke briskly. 'Put another shirt on. What about the Chicago Bears?'

'Right!' Chris turned to run up the steps and halted on the third one up. 'Gosh, I just thought of a funny thing. I wonder if she's horrible to that Marisa too? Maybe she just cares about Uncle Tom.'

Deborah shook her head, though that thought had

occurred to her too. 'I don't know, but listen to me, Chris, that's all Tommy's business. Mrs Mangan is entirely different with him and I've seen her when she's very charming.'

'Yes, but I've seen her when she's raving mad, that's the trouble.'

'And you'll tell no one!' Deborah reminded him.

'All right. Can I have Coke today instead of milk?'

'Just this once. I don't want you pouring soft drink down your throat, there's too much sugar in it.'

'But I need sugar for energy!' He flew up the stairs and leaned over the banister. 'Cal's going to take me over to Mr Sommerville's place soon. He said I have tons of potential.'

'*Mr McGovern!*' she corrected.

'No, Cal!'

'You're supposed to call him Mr McGovern. It's more respectful.'

'He *told* me to call him Cal. He likes me. I spoke to him the other night when he rang for Uncle Tom. He's very easy to speak to.'

'You never told me,' she said quickly.

'Are you sure I didn't? Anyway, how far do you think we'll go?'

'Oh, maybe a thousand miles! Now scat. Get a hat and put sandals on your feet. We'll leave as soon as I put a few things in the Esky.'

'Beaut!' His golden-skinned face brightened all of a sudden, the unpleasantness of the morning lost in a delicious excitement.

Leaning on the car door, Cal McGovern saw the Triumph swing up the drive and he drew in his breath, pressure lines around his nose and well-defined mouth. This wasn't going to be pleasant; just another incident in a long, weary day. They saw him at once and Chris waved, his good-looking, rather sombre little face touched with a brilliant smile.

'Hi!'

Cal raised his own hand, thinking how the child's whole face lit up when he smiled. He bore no special resemblance to his sister, but both of them had that radiant smile. Instead of going into the garage Deborah pulled off the drive and ran the car in under the jacarandas. It was after five, yet there was still a lot of heat in the sun. Both of them got out and Cal watched them. Chris was still wearing his bright smile but Deborah looked as wary as a fawn, her young slender body projecting her tensions.

'What brings you here, Mr McGovern?'

Chris looked up at her reprovingly. 'Call him Cal. If *I* can, *you* can. We had a beaut day. We've been everywhere and we had a picnic by the lake. I'll be back in a minute to tell you more, but first I have to feed the pups. Where's the key, Debby?'

'Here!' She held it out to him, seeing something disturbing behind Cal McGovern's unreadable expression. Chris took the key and danced away, mindful now of his responsibilities and the hearty appetite of labradors.

'You're coming in?' Deborah asked automatically, her colour heightening under his sharp, challenging gaze.

'If I may.'

'Why, certainly. You're our second visitor today.'

'So I believe.'

'Ah!' She gave a faint sigh. 'News travels fast.'

'Unfortunately. I don't go looking for it, it comes to me.'

She tilted her head back to look up at him, her skin burning. 'Is something wrong?'

'Nothing serious,' he said, flicking her collar down, 'just the usual petty conflicts. I had a call from Marisa.'

'She must ring you practically every day.'

He gave a decidedly dangerous little laugh and his

white teeth snapped. 'I hope you know I'm a very busy man. It's considered a great victory to get through to me.'

'I must remember not to call you at the office, then. Is there anything significant in your statement? I mean that Mrs Mangan was here this morning.'

He rubbed an unconscious finger over the deep cleft in his chin. 'It takes a lot to rattle me usually, but you, Deborah, have an uncanny knack, however ... Marisa told me that her mother was terribly upset when she came home. She went straight to her room and wouldn't speak for hours.'

'That must have been a break for everyone!'

'Apparently,' he said, ignoring her, 'Chris had worked himself into a temper and been very rude to her.'

'What about me?' she challenged sarcastically.

'She didn't say anything about you.'

'You surprise me. At least I'd be able to defend myself.'

'Deborah, Deborah!' he said, and held up a restraining hand. 'For the first time I can see your red-headed temper. I even think I like it. At least you've come gloriously alive. Do you think I *want* to come here and talk about Chris's behaviour?'

'You must, seeing that you're here!' she retorted.

'He can't go around being rude to adults, especially very stylish, temperamental ladies. It's not considered normal.'

'Are you going to hear his side of the story?'

'Certainly I am.'

'Then not from him, I assure you. I won't have him upset again.'

'It's no bother, truly! Don't be too protective, Deborah. Chris is growing up now. *Let* him!'

She flushed angrily, her dark green eyes brilliant. 'What exactly did Marisa tell you?'

'Just what I've said,' he answered mildly, 'but at considerable length. I had to get my secretary to invent a phone call!'

'Why Marisa?' she asked him.

'Eve was reluctant to speak for herself.'

'To hell with that!'

'Really, Deborah, you're a fabulous creature when you're angry. I'll have to see more of you.'

'Why should Marisa run to you with her little tittle-tales?'

'She's been running to me for a good few years now!' he said smoothly.

'Then why don't you marry her, for God's sake?'

'Why don't you mind your own business?' he warned her, a flash in his silvery eyes.

'I guess if I can, you can!' she snapped back. 'Mrs Mangan came here this morning and was extremely unpleasant. I don't intend to discuss it beyond the fact that she deliberately provoked Chris into being rude to her.'

'You've no objection if I speak to him?'

'You'll have to go past *me*!' she said, her hair a silken tangle about her face and her cheeks burning.

'Which is nothing at all!'

She stumbled a little in her haste to get away from him, only that minute conscious of all his dark, frightening energy, but he moved much too swiftly, caught her up and lifted her aside like a china doll. 'I always suspected you had a lot of fire in you, Deborah. Now I know!'

'I don't want you to upset Chris,' she said, inexplicably excited by his touch.

'Did I say I was going to? Settle down, you're too excitable. All I'm going to do is ask him a few questions. With your consent, I hope, though I'm notorious for getting my own way.'

'I can accept that, and I've only known you a short time.'

'I suppose satiny skin is bound to be sensitive. Won't you do as I ask?'

'You can't charm me!' she got out before she could help herself.

'Yes, I can, and I've a great idea!'

'I thought you came here to speak to Chris?'

'So I did, but the same old magic is beginning to work.'

She lowered her head, especially not wanting to remember, and the late afternoon radiance made a blazing aureole of her hair. 'Come in!' she said quietly.

He nodded casually and walked companionably beside her as they entered the house. 'I like the orchids. Your idea?'

'No, yours. Mandevilla sets the standards.'

'They're doing particularly well. Orchids don't like to be shut up, neither do roses. Remind me to send you some. Dark red, perfumed, velvety to the touch.'

Chris came up from the basement at a furious, breakneck speed. 'Boy, were they glad to see me! I'm glad you're here, Mr McGovern—Cal,' he said shyly. 'I was telling Debby you were going to take me along to Mr Sommerville's place.'

'So I am. I've already spoken to Harry. I've got one or two questions, Chris, I want to ask you first.'

'Go right ahead!'

'Please!' Deborah protested rather feverishly.

'Allow the boy to speak,' Cal said quietly.

'What is it?' Chris looked from one to the other, warning signals ringing in his head. 'Is it about Mrs Mangan?'

'Yes!' Cal said briefly. 'It transpires she's upset. God knows I don't want to buy into this, but there are a few things I must find out in Tom's absence. You know Mrs Mangan's daughter, Chris?'

'Yes.'

'Well, she rang me an hour ago to say that her mother

had visited you this morning and came home dreadfully upset. She, Mrs Mangan, claims you were extremely rude to her. Is this true?'

'She started it!' Chris said, beginning to swallow.

'Then you were.'

'Don't answer, Chris!' Deborah said indignantly, loving him so much that she burned with it.

'But I *want* to. I want Cal to understand. Mrs Mangan came and she gave me a present. Capsela, you know. It's really great—anyway, I gave it back to her. I made up a power boat and I was coming back to show it to Debby and her when I heard what she was saying. I couldn't believe it for a moment, then I saw her face. She really hates Debby and now I guess she hates me. I don't care. I'm a man!'

'What did she say?' Cal asked calmly, regarding the boy with a level stare.

'I've forbidden Chris to talk about it,' Deborah said sharply. 'Let the tide wash it away!'

'You considered Mrs Mangan was attacking your sister?' Cal continued, holding the boy's eyes.

'She sure was! She said . . .'

'Chris!' Deborah cut him off in mid-sentence, looking so sad and vulnerable that Chris shrugged his shoulders.

'I can't tell you, Mr McGovern.'

'Then tell me what *you* said!'

'I called her a bitch!'

'To her face?' The winged black eyebrows shot up.

'No. I don't remember saying anything rude to her face. I just told her that if she hurt Debby I'd find a way to hurt her, and I would too!'

'Good God!'

'Please don't ask him any more questions. Please, Cal, don't!'

'That's the first time you've called me by my name. I wish you two children lived some place else. All right,

Chris, I've heard your side of the story and I believe you. But don't think that gives you the all clear to engage in slanging matches with grown-ups, I expect you to behave at all times. That's what growing up is all about—control. I don't go around having punch-ups with my competitors!'

'I bet you'd beat them!' Chris said admiringly.

'Care to get me a drink, Deborah?' Cal turned to her. 'It's been a long day.'

'Won't you come and see the pups while Debby's getting it?' Chris begged. 'Perhaps you could stay for dinner. Debby's a super cook!'

'What an excellent idea! You're a very smart girl, Miss Nugent.' Cal faced her mockingly, dark and compelling. Something in her expression made him smile and he clenched a bronze fist and thumped his forehead with it. 'She seems to be shrivelling me with her green eyes. Perhaps if you ask her, Chris, on my behalf!'

'It would be a cinch for Deb to set an extra plate. Wouldn't it, Deb?'

Her great eyes embraced her brother. It was clear that he was desperately anxious to please this new hero-figure.

'Do you want to stay, Mr McGovern?' she asked in a cool little voice.

'I might as well seeing you can't manage without me. Now, Chris, we'll see the pups, then I have to make a few phone calls. After that I'll help you get dinner.'

'I think it's undesirable to have more than one person in the kitchen,' Deborah said sweetly, 'but thank you for offering.'

'Oh well!' he said, looking round and walking over to the large abstract painting she had so recently hung, 'then I'll simply dive into the pool with Chris. What do you say, young feller?'

'That would be beaut!'

'I'm glad one of you likes me,' Cal said wryly.

'One must take the bitter with the better!' Deborah said smoothly, and suddenly smiled, to her immense surprise irresistibly drawn to him. He looked at her for a moment and it seemed as though the walls were closing in, sweeping them both together to the centre of the room. It was a curious feeling, for he hadn't moved away from the painting. Her pulses leaped urgently, and the sight of him seared into her. If she didn't move quickly she wouldn't be able to save herself.

'Right, Chris!' she said briskly. 'Show Cal the pups, and I imagine he'll want to know where Uncle Tom keeps his togs. If you'll both excuse me a few moments I'd like to tidy up. I feel very dishevelled.'

'There's really no need to be anxious,' Cal said without hesitation. 'A little dishevelment can be very beguiling.'

Something had to release her from this rapt feeling. Perhaps she had had too much sun, for an exquisite slow heat was still arrowing along her spine. She turned away from them without another word and ran lightly up the stairs, hearing Chris's voice floating up to her:

'I know I'd never be able to beat you!'

'Still, you might as well try!' Cal answered, the merest suggestion of a smile in his voice.

Deborah went quickly along the corridor to her room. She too would have liked a dip in the pool, instead she would have to make do with a quick shower. She had started out like a fire-breathing dragon when Cal had acted and spoken with extreme moderation. It was terrible what she was doing to herself, for her heart was thumping. Ten minutes later, bathed and refreshed and dressed in a very becoming strapless sundress with a ruched top, she went downstairs to fix their guest a drink. She really didn't know what he would like so she would have to ask him. They were already in the pool and she went out through the sun room and across the grass, calling:

'What kind of drink would you like?'

'A nice long beer!' Cal pulled himself out of the water and sat on the side, just staring at Deborah as she came to realise she was staring at him. He was deeply bronzed, his lean powerful body in splendid condition. He looked so good it made her hover uncertainly, looking not unlike a gorgeous butterfly in her flower-printed dress.

'Get yourself something and come out here,' he invited.

'Make mine a ginger ale!' Chris called.

'Think you can concentrate on the order?' Cal's silvery grey gaze narrowed over her and his mouth had a twist to it, goading her into some kind of a response.

'I've half a mind to push you in!' she snapped.

'Why don't you?'

'You'd retaliate.'

'Never! I told you you'd have to beg me, remember?'

Her green eyes glowed brighter and the sudden colour in her cheeks told of swift-running emotions. 'I know you won't believe this, but my mind has gone blank. I can't remember anything.'

'Then I suppose I'll have to do it again,' he threatened.

'You've got a predatory streak, haven't you?'

'Yes, an implacable, predatory streak, and you, of course, are as captive as ever!'

'Strange,' she said, whirling about, 'I feel as free as the breeze.'

His laugh followed her and she covered the lawn and the terrace with tremendous, gazelle-like speed. These flippant, sophisticated exchanges were beyond her. There was purpose in everything he did and he was lulling her with his mocking charm. He probably made the blood course through Marisa's veins just as brightly. Some men could touch a woman's senses very easily; it was a gift, like an attractive speaking voice. Probably, she reflected, he was playing some dreadful cat-and-mouse game with her.

Carefully she made herself up a Campari and soda, placed a small glass of ginger ale beside it on the silver tray, then took a bottle of beer from the refrigerator in the brand Tom favoured, and a crystal beer-glass from the cabinet. It would be a miracle if they could get through the evening as pleasantly as it was starting, but after all they did, in an extraordinarily uncomplicated and carefree atmosphere that Deborah, if no one else, failed to understand. Did one break bread with one's enemy and thoroughly enjoy it? And afterwards in the pulsing darkness turn up one's face like a girl in a dream, yearning for a hard, disturbing mouth to settle upon it? That it didn't did not astonish her, but she would die of shame before she would beg Cal McGovern for anything!

# CHAPTER SEVEN

Around the coral cay the fringing reef formed a a great herringbone pattern woven by countless galaxies of coral polyps through many millions of years. The skirting coral sands beneath the softly whispering coconut palms were a blinding sun-bleached white and the surrounding waters had a clarity and depth of colour, a heavenly deep blue shading to green in the shallows, that Deborah found piercingly beautiful. Paradise had been aptly named, an extravagantly beautiful natural wonder and part of the Great Barrier Reef, the twelve-hundred-mile miracle that stretched along the coast of Queensland; once a sailor's nightmare, as Captain James Cook found to his sorrow, now—with charts that warned of the presence of treacherous reefs—a grand canal for the tourist liners and the big game fishermen of the world.

There were many visitors to the island; the yachtsmen and the fishermen, of course, a few American movie stars, the lovers of sun and surf in idyllic surroundings, the shell-collectors and those that found the million different designs of corals a source of wonder and enjoyment, but no visitors strayed near the private McGovern compound without an invitation. The luxurious Paradise Cay Hotel stood at the other end of the island and both faced the big deep lagoon.

In the few days they had been on the island Deborah had felt profoundly at peace, the haunting sadness of the long preceding months eased by nature at its most beautiful and benign. Here on this exquisite little island her spirits began to lift, and Chris was revelling in it, his dark curls perpetually tangled with sea-water, his tan deepening to an incredibly smooth and even dark gold. Her own white skin needed extra protection and Mr Robert McGovern had presented her with an enormous Chinese coolie hat that turned her eyes to an elfin green. At going on eighty, he still had an eye for a beautiful woman, and these days he considered young Deborah looked dazzling, more rested and relaxed, the faint melancholy of her lovely face replaced by more and more flashes of her natural youthful vitality. The young weren't meant to mourn for ever and she was more sensitive than most.

A fiendishly private person for all his supposed gregariousness, Robert considered inviting the girl and her young brother a triumph. He hadn't felt so alive and interested in things himself for many a long day. There was so much to show them and they made a wonderfully appreciative audience, marvelling at the house with all its splendid comforts, and beyond its colourful, shrub-studded perimeter, the brilliance of the reef with its coral gardens and incredibly beautiful little fish, gaudy as butterflies, and the scores of gemlike shell that Chris had begun collecting, his mouth falling open at the size of the giant clams and the green turtles.

Their days started early and finished late, but after all it was holidays and Robert was enjoying their company immensely. He even had had a piano sent over from the hotel for Deborah's use, though it weighed a ton.

His grandson and Tom were expected on Christmas Eve. With a five-million dollar net profit on one of their riskiest ventures, they could afford to relax. These days he left most things to Robert. His grandson would inherit his millions and all his responsibilities to the State and the country and his thousands of employees. Robert would know what to do when he died. Once it had seemed to him that his world had been shattered when his son was killed, but Robert was even more like him than Cam, his beloved Cameron, had ever been. Robert was ready for anything, brilliant and ambitious and entirely serious about maintaining, indeed expanding, the McGovern empire. The crippling long hours, the responsibilities, the grinding shocks and the tensions, the bouquets and the brickbats, the high level intrigue and the jealousies, didn't seem to affect him. He revelled in big business as young Christopher revelled in the water. It was a natural gift and very few people had it. Tom was a very capable and trustworthy top executive, but he wouldn't survive at the head of the table. Tom he had taken up and shown him success, but even now he knew in his heart that Tom didn't need this kind of life. He could say to hell with big business any day and not miss it; it was the Mc-Governs' life's blood. That was the difference.

Tom he had taken to immediately, all those years ago, and this holiday would confirm or deny his own and his grandson's opinion. Mr McGovern felt quite suddenly that a man couldn't blame Tom. Deborah was an unusual girl, beautiful and gifted with every quality in a woman that mattered. Still, it couldn't be. Robert had suggested he might put a suite aside in the hotel for Eve Mangan and her daughter, but damn it all, he had never liked Eve, and Paradise was his private retreat from the world. If there had to be complications he didn't want them on the island.

It would be a great relief in one way if Tom did marry the woman, but it would surprise him all the same. A solution had to be reached, otherwise his name wasn't Big Bob McGovern. Maybe he should have accepted that knighthood after all. He would have if only Evelyn hadn't died. She would have enjoyed calling him Sir Robert, though she was the one with the impeccable background. He had fought his way up from nowhere.

Deborah, climbing up the flight of steps from the beach, her long legs glossed with salt and sand, caught him dreaming. They sat together on the long bench that was his favourite vantage point and looked out over the beautiful lagoon with its enclosing reef. It was deliciously cool under the canopy of pisonia trees and the inclining pandanus, their view of the blue water framed by dazzling vistas of flowers; the hibiscus and oleanders, the white ginger blossom and gardenias, the allamanda and the fragrant waxy frangipani of every colour and variety, and, growing right down almost to the water line, the salt-resistant, dark red bottle brush with its dark green and silver leaves, called in New Zealand the pohutukawa.

'This is Paradise, isn't it?' Deborah said after about half a minute.

'My favourite place in all the world,' the old man agreed. 'I needed somewhere I could relax from all the demands that became part of my life. This place has been necessary for me over the years. Now of course it caters to weary businessmen from all over the world; they love the life, the tropical environment, the fishing. A man has to have an escape route. Life by the sea is glorious, ever-changing. When Robert comes he can show you lots of things I can't, like the best of the coral gardens. They're about a hundred yards out. He can take you out there. We've seen it from the glass-bottomed boat, but when you're down there with a snorkel and flippers it's like being in a wonderful new world—you can't imagine. No worries about swimming underwater?'

'I don't think so.'

'Robert will look after you. You just have to breathe through the snorkel and do what you're told. He can take Christopher out another time, or Tom can. He needs to be watched exclusively or he'd just take off. Swims like a fish, doesn't he?'

'A natural!' Deborah smiled, shaking the hair out of her eyes. 'I can't thank you enough for inviting us. It's been wonderful.'

'And it will get better, my dear. You've been very good for me too.'

'Life is strange, isn't it?' she asked him. 'My mother brought Tommy to us, and because of him we're here with you!'

'There's usually a reason for these things,' Robert said, nodding his silver head. 'I suppose you could say—fate.'

'Anyway, we're very grateful to both of you!' she said in a low voice. 'Tommy is a very fine man.'

'Don't I know it! He's a fine sailor and a lot of fun too; that's what brought us together. He's different too, in a way. He doesn't want what a lot of men strive for, success in their field, a lot of money. Perhaps if his life had been different,' he said softly. 'Your mother must have been a very beautiful woman!'

'I adored her!' Deborah said, a warm tear sliding down her cheek.

'So apparently did he, because he never forgot her.'

They both sat there for a moment saying nothing, then the old man dropped a friendly, bracing hand on her shoulder.

'Right-oh now, what about a bit of lunch? We don't have to catch it the hard way, either. I saw Lee come up with a string of coral trout. By the way, where's the young fellow? I hope he hasn't run off at a time like this. My early morning swim has made me hungry.'

'Me too,' said Deborah. 'There's nothing like it. I shall put on weight!'

'Should you not? You're a featherweight. A puff of wind would blow you away!'

'It won't at the end of the holiday!' Deborah laughed. 'Chris is down on the beach. I'll go and get him.'

'And I'll fetch out a nice fresh Reisling. Hunter Valley, I think. Splendid with seafood. One mustn't over-chill white wine. Remember that when you're an extravagantly successful hostess. A slightly chilled wine refreshes, but a freezing one burns.'

'I'll certainly remember it!' she smiled at him, the sea breeze tossing flame-coloured curls around her frangipani skin, so young and so innocently beautiful for a moment that the old man felt an actual stab of pain. 'But I doubt if I'll ever make a society hostess!'

'Why not?' he asked enigmatically. 'Our paths have crossed. I've a fancy, young Deborah, that you belong in the McGovern world!'

She looked back at him intently, but he wasn't smiling, his grey eyes absorbed with his own thoughts. She slicked a hand over her unruly curls, then turned to run down the beach stairs. Both McGoverns had a charm that was almost compulsive. Tomorrow Tommy and Cal would be here, and as she thought that her heart began thudding and an odd excitement welled up in her.

'Chris?' she called.

He had his back to her, half-reclining on the white sand to watch Digby and Wags have a tug-o'-war over one of his sneakers. 'Don't let them do that!' she exclaimed urgently. 'That must be the third pair. Labradors love chewing things, and they have slippers of their own!'

'They don't seem to be happy with them. They prefer mine.'

'Well, they just so happen to be the only pair I've brought to the island, and you need them to protect your feet when we explore the reef!'

'Gosh, this is a beautiful place!' said Chris, running his hand through the sand. 'It's fantastic that Mr

McGovern invited us. He must like us!'

'Of course he does. Now stop that!' she called defensively as Wags made a playful leap for her, leaving white scratch marks on her legs. 'Come on, Chris, you grab Digby. Mr McGovern wants his lunch!'

'Fine!' he said simply, cuddling the golden, growling puppy. 'I want mine!'

They were all down at the beach to see *Jabirus II* come in through the niggerheads, leaping for the fast-running channel, then rolling in with the white foaming breakers. It looked like a dream, a beautiful ocean-going yacht, its two tall masts billowing with sail.

'Perfect!' The old man shouted gleefully, and clapped Chris on the shoulder.

The boy was literally shaking with excitement, his enthusiasm for once in his life diverted from motor cars. 'It's just like the sea picture you have at the house!'

'You like it?'

'Yes, I do.'

'A very highly esteemed marine painter did that for me. That's *Jabirus I*. I sold it a few years ago to a rich American staying at the hotel—made a nice profit, I'm happy to say. *Jabirus II* has a lot more refinements, sophisticated navigational and communication equipment. It's beautifully finished too, with hand-rubbed woods and bronze hardware. Of course it was a lot more expensive, but one can see that both yachts had the same designer.'

'It's fabulous, like an epic or something!' Chris answered, in thrall. 'Funny, I've never thought much about boats.'

The old man snorted like a warhorse and twisted his head to look down at the boy. 'They're just as good as motor cars—better. With eleven thousand miles of coastline surrounding this great island of ours, Australia, boats are just the same as beaches. The sea is incredibly beautiful, the ultimate experience. You're at home in the water. You swim like a fish. We'd better get you started shouldering a pair of oars, and you can work your way up from there. Your Uncle Tom is a fine sailor and Robert is one of our leading yachtsmen. Why, don't you know *Jabirus II* took line honours in the Sydney to Hobart?'

'No, I didn't. That's marvellous!'

'It is indeed, even if I say so myself!' Robert turned his head and looked over to the devoted Lee, who had the runaway ready. 'Don't stand there grinning, get out to the boys!'

Lee bowed gracefully, then jumped into the small boat and started up the engine. It fired immediately, then went tearing across the mirror-like surface of the blue lagoon to where the yacht was nosing into anchorage about four hundred yards out.

'That must be thrilling,' Chris cried.

'There'll be plenty of time for you to go out. The boys will have some gear to bring back with them. There, Lee's holding her steady, they'll be back in no time. You're very quiet, Deborah, everything all right?'

'It should be in a little while,' she answered. 'That was a very stirring sight—it sort of swept me in. It must be a soaring satisfaction to handle a boat like that.'

"Good girl, so it is!' the old man answered approvingly. 'Mind you, Rob's a bit reckless. He's supremely sure of himself, but there's no denying his mastery. I'm very proud of him. More proud than I can say!'

Deborah reacted spontaneously to this open display of love and slipped her arm through the old man's. 'I think Rob is very fortunate in his grandfather. You're very much alike.'

'So I've been told,' he agreed. 'Can't say I always see it, especially when he's contradicting me to my face. I never did that with my father, but then he died when I wasn't much more than a wee lad. Rob will go far. He might even outshine his grandfather!'

'No!' Deborah said, and smiled at him.

'You know, lassie, you're a siren!' The old man halted, looking down at her face with the McGovern piercing attention. 'No question about it! Ah, here they come now. Let's go down to the water's edge. It's the most beautiful morning imaginable, isn't it? Perfect Christmas weather. Tonight we'll have a little party! Could be we might even let you stay up, young Christopher.'

'No later than ten!' Deborah chimed in, reacting like a sister.

'Just as your sister says. She's the boss. My God! Will you look at Rob? He looks just like a pirate. Both of them have changed their clothes, but really there's no need for him to wear anything with a tear in it!'

'Maybe that's the Scot in him!' Deborah said teasingly. 'I'm sure it's perfectly good elsewhere.'

'Now, that's very naughty!' the old man answered her, clicking his tongue at his grandson's raffish appearance. Cal had jumped out when there was water up to his knees, raising his arm in welcome. The old man and the boy returned his salute with equal camaraderie, but Deborah felt suddenly panicky. In another minute Cal had reached the beach, his long arm shooting out to encircle his grandfather's neck and thump his shoulder.

'You're still here, you old devil!'

'I'd hate to think what would happen to the business if I wasn't. How goes it?'

'Exceeding our hopes. I'll tell you at the house. Deborah, Chris, how are you both?' Silvery-grey eyes in a rugged dark face swept over them, delighting Chris and thoroughly confusing his sister. 'I don't really have to ask. Chris, your skin is turning to chocolate. Come on, there's Tom splashing out now. Go and meet him and bring back one of the bags!' He loped up the beach in his torn blue shirt and cream slacks, looking to Deborah's mind terribly elegant, then halted beside her and lifted her chin. 'Your eyes are as green as an underwater cavern. Miss me?'

'No, not particularly,' she said softly.

'That would be dampening, only I know you're lying. A little pulse has just woken up in your throat!'

'You're very observant.'

'You're very easy to observe, Lorelei!' He turned his crisply curled black head and looked down the beach. 'Step out now and greet Tom. Keep it calm!'

'You don't change, do you?' she hissed like a small cat.

'Admit you love me just the way I am,' he teased.

'However likely that may be with a long line of others, you're wrong now!'

'It's not possible!' he exclaimed, sparkling mockery in the depths of his eyes. 'Of course, you haven't developed properly as a woman. It's your immense good fortune that I'm here now. We'll go for a stroll on the beach to-night.'

'I would rather go with anyone else in the whole wide world!' she said, making a funny little strangling noise.

'That's an infallible giveaway.' His eyes fairly blazed in his sea-tanned face; his lean powerful body was immensely vital and graceful, the sky-blue shirt unbuttoned to the waist, the rolled-up cuffs of his slacks soaked—and he didn't give a darn.

'What makes you so arrogant?' she challenged him.

'But my dear Deborah, haven't you heard about my successes?' he asked innocently.

'They don't impress me!'

'Good for you.' He smiled with lazy impudence into her face. 'Now it's Tom's turn, but do be careful.'

'Fiend!' she looked back at him, her delicately-boned

face colouring, then she spun on her heel and ran lightly across the glittery white coral sand to Tom, raising herself on tiptoe and kissing his cheek.

'How are you, Tommy? We've missed you!'

He smiled appreciatively into her warmly tinted face. 'I've missed you too. My, you do look well—radiant. Chris too. The boy is thriving. You've done a great deal of good in this world, Bob. You're bound to go to heaven!'

'I hope it's interesting,' the old man chuckled. 'Let's get up to the house and talk and talk!'

'Boy, it's good to be here!' Tom gave a heartfelt sigh, slipping an arm round Deborah and Chris and walking them up the beach. 'This is really something, isn't it, kids?'

'Beaut!' Chris returned, squeezing Tom's middle. 'Do you think Cal would let me look over the yacht?'

'Better still, I'm sure he'll take a snap of you at the helm.'

Chris started to skip with delight. 'I certainly am glad you came to get us, Uncle Tom!'

'Destiny!' Tom said, unconsciously echoing his old friend.

Their little celebration turned into a brilliant success with serious attention to the food and the wine, all served in the remarkable cool and beautiful loggia overlooking the ocean. They were all in a relaxed, easy mood; the three men obviously relished one another's company with the added bonus of having a young girl and a small boy to tell their stories to, and enjoyed their enthralled, faintly incredulous expressions considering that every one of their stories was true; their experiences of sailing and big game fishing, their tussles with cyclones and an anxiety-ridden trip to rescuing the survivors of a yacht that had run aground on Paradise reef during the last big blow. A sleepy-eyed Chris had been packed off to bed shortly before ten when the old man, in fine form, decided that he wanted to play cards. Tom, grinning his approval, began to set up the table, but Cal told them very nonchalantly to start without him as Deborah had been pestering him all evening to take her for a stroll on the beach.

Tom, tanned and relaxed after an afternoon spent lolling on the beach, told them to go right ahead, and pushed back the ceiling-high shutters to let the beautiful flow of sea air right into the loggia. Outside, beyond the balcony, a silvery moon rode high, shimmering over the great expanse of water, a huge flowering poinciana darkly etched against the sky and framed by the shutters, the flawless great trusses of flowers glowing scarlet where the light from the magnificent shell chandelier fell upon them.

'Coming?' Cal asked the speechless girl, his gaze frankly mocking.

She looked doubtful and twisted her head back over her shoulder to look at the others, but they were already examining the hands Tom had dealt them.

'Don't look round for a way out!' Cal warned, and grasped her wrist rather tautly. 'You won't find it unless it's over the top. Quite a drop!'

'I can't walk in these sandals,' she protested.

'You don't need shoes on the beach.'

'I mean I won't be able to walk down the stairs.'

'I'll carry you,' he offered.

'No, you won't! They're quite all right after all.'

Cal's crystal-clear gaze was dazzling as it rested on her face and her throat, the creamy sand-coloured long dress with its low rouleau-tied neck and cutaway shoulders, its softly draped folds clinging to her slender figure. It was an enormously successful colour with Deborah's skin and hair, and he complimented her again, ignoring her baffling reluctance and the darkly green eyes shadowed by her heavy lashes.

'You can't afford not to grow up,' he said candidly.

'I can take it in easy stages.'

'Now, what does that mean?'

His sparkling eyes seemed to be raking her and the hot colour flooded. 'It means,' she said rather desperately, 'that you're far too sophisticated for me and you shouldn't be enjoying it.'

'When I've come to your rescue?'

She shook her head, trying to gauge his expression. 'How could you? I'm not in any danger.'

'That's what you think! A girl like you can't be too careful.'

Her eyes, wide and troubled, flew to his, jade green and dominating the delicate oval of her face. 'Occasionally I don't understand a word you're saying!' she said.

'Why should you?' His hard expression relaxed and he looked at her lazily. 'You're just a curly-headed girl-child. I'd forgotten. A thousand things suggest themselves to me, but I'll need to bite back my comments.'

'I hope so, if they're going to be hurtful.'

'You think I want to hurt you, don't you?' Cal took her arm and led her out to the circular terrace.

'I think you've made it your misson!' she pointed out, but wouldn't look at him. 'You know, scouting ahead and putting up big signs. *Danger. Dead End. No Through Road.* That kind of thing!'

'Perhaps,' he said lightly, not disagreeing. 'Maybe I think you're in need of them!'

'Believe me, I don't wish to cause any trouble.'

'But it suits you beautifully!'

The outside lighting fell on her hair and the side of her face, lending her skin a luminous lily-like quality. 'Damn!' she said, and made a delicate little movement away from his hand. 'I don't know why I'm coming.'

'Yes, you do!'

A tremor shook her at the note in his voice and she went quickly down the stairs to the shrub-studded lawn.

'Don't go sprinting away,' he cautioned.

'I should when you're in this mood.'

'What mood, tell me?'

'Oh, you feel very relaxed and you've broken away from all the stress of the week——'

'Then there's no mad rush to get this walk over!'

'I love it here,' was all she could think of saying. All around them the coconut palms were waving their tall fronds, and the perfume of the ginger blossom and the sweet gardenias mingled with the salt-scented air, the creamy white flowers glowed mystically from their thick dark foliage. It was blissful and Deborah stood there for a moment, closing her eyes and filling her lungs with the fragrant tangy air. 'I really believe it has helped me; the peace and the beauty, the sun and the sea!'

He looked down at her face so beautifully dreamy, the whole set of her young body indefinably yearning. 'I'm glad,' he said crisply as though stirred by the delicate pathos of her face and voice. 'You do, in fact, look better than I expected. More the way you should look. You see, little one, one door shuts and another opens.'

'Yes, it's like some kind of release.'

'Think you can make it down the stairs? It's fairly steep for high-heeled sandals.'

'No need to worry, I'll make it!' A night bird screeched and flew through the trees, and she pushed back against his hard shoulder in sudden alarm. 'That startled me!'

'Good, I like it!' His arm slipped across her and drew her back lightly against him.

She dropped her head forward, grasping his arm. 'Remember your promise!'

'I don't think I want to. All right, don't fret, I'll let you go.'

'It's an advantage to be a man and so strong,' she said. 'An unfair advantage.'

'At least let me take the lead down the steps. Give me your hand.'

She surrendered it and a flare of sensuality shot through her that was almost frightening. Every inch of her skin was prickling with sensation. He didn't look back at her, but held the branches of the flowering shrubs, not speaking until they reached the beach. Deborah bent down and kicked off her sandals and he settled them on a rock. The stars were brightly blossoming, thickly clustered over the ocean, the long graceful line of the *Jabirus* glowing luminously in the silvery-lemon moonlight. Legions of tiny crabs scuttled for cover, disturbed by their footsteps, and the wind through the long spiky leaves of the pandanus made a curious little song plaintive and foreign.

Something seemed to unfurl in Deborah, some exquisite tide of feeling, for she turned her head sideways, lifted one arm above it and executed a chain of near-perfect pirouettes to the wind-song.

'That must have taken a lot of practice!' Cal said, following her up, very tall and disturbing, his dark face in shadow.

'Yes, it did, and a lot of dizzy falls. I learned ballet for ten years.'

'Also the piano.'

'My mother believed in accomplishments,' she told him, 'they were expected. She even had the T.V. moved out of the house so we could fall back on our own resources. How do you think Chris got to be such a good swimmer? He joined a training squad, while the other kids in his class were watching the cartoons!'

He laughed. 'I guess it would make it easier. Admirable, too, with all the junk they're fed on. What are you going to do with Tom's T.V.?'

'Chris and I don't see much of it, except the things I mark with red pencil—fun things too, providing they're imaginative. I detest violence and the T.V. is creating so many difficulties for children. They try to relate it to their own lives.'

'You're a very strong-minded girl!' he smiled.

'I hope that's in order,' she snapped.

'I'm not a bit surprised!'

'Oh?' she half turned to glance at him, 'I thought you might scorn strong-mindedness in a woman?'

'Not if she combines it with other things!'

The night seemed fraught with excitement, a surge of desire that shook her with its intensity. She hardly knew this man, yet she felt as though she had known him for ever. Her feelings were utterly confused. Part of her appealed to him not to hurry her or jolt her into a sensual awakening, the other was all provocation, an ardency that was strong in her. She had been so eager for him to arrive and somehow she had shown it. The longing for him to take her in his arms was becoming too great, and her feminine pride put up a fight for survival.

She moved ahead of him along the coral strand, the breeze cooling her body. The waters surrounding the reef glowed with a magical phosphorescence thrown off by all the luminous little sea creatures. It looked extraordinary, quite visible but ghostly, with the black line of the nigger-heads and the white foaming line of surf.

Inside the reef it was a flat calm, the water scarcely lapping the sides of the *Jabirus*. The breeze was a caress, the unsleeping south-east trade. Deborah felt incredibly happy and afraid; a mass of contradictions. How could one deny and invite at the same time? The thick fringing vegetation looked like a jungle at night, the hotel at the further end of the island like a ship at sea, quite brilliant, and there was the sound of music.

'Who are you running away from?' Cal asked her, closing the gap between them.

'Myself!'

His voice was sharply amused. 'Then stop it! For all you know I may not even be considering a romantic interlude.'

'And I'll have you know I'm certainly not!'

'That's absurd, isn't it?' He looked down at her in the old, arrogant way, laughter sparkling in his eyes.

She turned away with a show of poise, remarking on the bright lights from the hotel. 'I've never seen it!'

'I'll take you down one day. Or night, if you prefer. I don't usually go near there unless I have to. Women take a fanatical interest in a well-heeled bachelor!'

'Tough!' she said, and smiled, a quirk in her voice.

'Well, it's tough keeping up a public image all the time. My grandfather is tiring of it.' Cal's voice changed. 'He's remarkable, I know, but lately I've started to worry about him. Don't for God's sake mention it, he'd be outraged. You've been good for him, Deborah. He looks as keen as he's done in a long while.'

'You should have been here the day he had the piano brought up from the hotel!' she laughed.

'I can imagine! What did he move to get it in? I still haven't figured it out.'

'It's a monster, I know.' She very nearly apologised. 'Full-size, but your grandfather insisted, and he gets so much pleasure out of listening. Actually it was the wooden temple dancer and the big Chinese screen. I put them in the loggia.'

He laughed softly. 'You soon get used to my grandfather. He can be a little frightening sometimes, to a lot of people.'

'Not to me!' she said gently.

'No, you're just the way he likes a woman, and to be a dazzling pianist! Perfect!'

'Is that some kind of little dig?'

'You take me too seriously.'

'Yes, I do!' She could feel his eyes on her face but she kept staring at the hotel. 'What does it feel like to be the heir to the McGovern fortunes?'

'Badly off sometimes,' he said, his voice low and humorous. 'I wouldn't mind a bit more leisure time, or a few more people I could really trust or let my guard down with!'

'Oh, come now,' she looked up at him seriously, 'I'm sure your staff are devoted to you.'

'I'm not talking about *our* people, you foolish child, I'm talking about the people I have to deal with. Some of them spend every waking minute trying to find a chink in my armour. They even employ other people to do it!'

'And is there one?'

He grinned. 'Not yet, anyway. Any more impossible questions, ma'am?'

Deborah's confusion vanished and she knew exactly what to say to floor him. 'Your grandfather would like nothing better than to see you married. Did you know that?'

'What is this, for God's sake?' he said with startling abruptness.

'Didn't you know?' Suddenly she was enjoying herself. 'He has a fantastic desire to see his great-grandson.'

Cal hesitated fractionally as though dumbfounded, then caught her arm and turned her to him. 'Do you know, Deborah, you could very well be right, seeing he's a great friend of yours. When did you receive this charming confidence?'

'Oh, people often tell me things!' she said airily. 'I should have thought you'd realise it yourself.'

'As a matter of fact I do!' he said smartly, and his hand tightened. 'How would you like to marry me and have my child?'

For an instant she was rigid with shock. 'Oh really, I didn't mean——'

'Why not?'

'I know perfectly well that this is your idea of a joke. There's a devilish streak in you. I've known it all along!'

'You brought it up,' he pointed out so crisply that she blinked.

'Well, I meant generally speaking. Not *me*, of course!'

'Let's see!' He put her in front of him, his hands on her shoulders, his back to the light. 'You're beautiful. You're even clever, and young enough to get in some solid years of training. It might be a golden opportunity for you.'

'It sounds more like a disaster!'

His eyes narrowed over her and he tacked on almost sarcastically. 'Why, you're more than halfway in love with me!'

'I don't even like you very much,' she retorted.

'Who's talking about liking? I'm not asking you to be fond of me, I'm talking about *donner und blitzen*!'

'I won't listen,' she said perversely, 'and incidentally, you're cracking my bones!'

'Stop complaining! You do a lot of that. I tell you, Deborah, I know you—you were involved in an instant. Just as long as it took you to decide you were going to make a fight of it!'

'You can joke, but I won't listen,' she argued. 'You can get married any time you like—to dozens of women, so what's the point of talking nonsense to me?'

'What's the point of talking at all? Words will only tangle us up. We could give a big party and announce our engagement.' He pulled her closer, holding her still.

'That wouldn't appeal to me at all!' she said, the soft furious colour mounting under her skin, for her little joke was rebounding. 'Anyway, I don't intend to marry for years yet!'

'It would be a nuisance to wait too long for you!' Cal

murmured, his brilliant eyes mocking.

Without even realising it she was resting against him. 'Why are you saying this?' she asked fretfully.

'I thought my chances were pretty good, and it would be a solution.'

'To what?' she demanded.

'To something that's bothering me. Do you think you could handle it?'

'You know very well I couldn't. The very thought fills me with shock!'

'Well, obviously you're too young for such an honour——'

'And I wouldn't dream of sacrificing myself either! I hope you'll be happy with some other person nearer your own age!'

'How disrespectful! No, Deborah, seriously, it's about time I married, and now that you've brought it to my attention I don't think I need look around any further. It won't be easy for either of us, I'm not entirely unmindful of the difficulties, but we only have to get through a day at a time. The night times won't be the slightest trouble!'

'Idiot!' she said, trying to find the strength to pull away.

'No, you might even enjoy being married to me.'

'Let me go!'

'No, never! He held her fast. 'Why don't you cool down, your skin is scorching. I'm not exactly insulting you!'

'No, this is simply one of your ghastly jokes!'

'Maybe the joke's on me,' he said tautly. 'I didn't particularly want to have anything to do with you, much less get in the deep end. I'm not sure you won't be a handful.'

'Please don't be stupid, Rob!' she said in a soft, pleading voice, as her impassioned struggles proved futile.

'You didn't warn me you were going to call me Rob!'

'It just slipped out—I've become so used to hearing your grandfather call you Robert.'

'Go ahead. Call me Robert!' There was a note in his voice she couldn't quite recognise.

'I don't want to say another word,' she said jerkily, an electric tension along her nerves.

'I don't intend to either, but nothing is going to stop me kissing you until you cry your eyes out,' he said grimly.

'You must be mistaking me for someone else. You *couldn't* make me cry.'

'No, you little rebel! You should be grateful. Practically everyone believes I'm one hell of a catch. It's maddening to listen to this kind of thing from you.'

'What about Marisa?' she said, as if it were some definite form of protection.

'Don't be like that, Deborah!' he chided her gently. 'After all, I'm quite free to ring the changes.'

'Well, I'd like you to know that I don't agree with chopping and changing. What's more, I know what's been going on.'

'That's an nasty crack,' Cal said aggressively. 'You'd better watch it. The truth is, if you require it, that I've never liked to see Marisa suffer unduly, so I've taken her out from time to time. I may even have kissed her, I can't be sure. You've confused my mind.'

'No,' she said crisply, 'no woman could do that. You've just started out on some wild scheme of your own!'

'Not wild,' he corrected, 'a winner. I always pick winners. There's a big difference.'

'The difficulty is that I'm not taking you seriously!'

'I haven't pushed you far enough, that's why! Turn up your mouth, that's a first step.'

Deborah bent her head forward, shaking a little. 'Please stop!' she begged.

146

'I haven't a chance!'

'I thought you were thoroughly controlled?'

'Too much control for too much of the time!' he said with curbed violence, his hands closing over her bare shoulders. 'I've been promising myself you whether you like it or not!'

'I'll tell your grandfather!' she said desperately as his dark face swam above her.

'I guess he knows.'

'I'll tell Tom!' she said, and began to cry.

'Don't you dare!' he said savagely, shifting his hand to the back of her head, shaping it and turning her face up towards him. 'There's a considerable difference between fooling around and meaning it. Why do you have to be so distracting? Why do you have to have skin like a gardenia and cry salty tears? Why do you have to have the sweetest, softest mouth ...'

The blood pounded in her ears, but she couldn't control her yearning. Cal's mouth caught hers in a fury of possession and she opened her own to him, her eyes closing. She made no resistance but fitted herself to him, beyond pretending. He was showing her passion and a faint violence, holding her implacably even though she was yielding, so that when her mouth was momentarily free she whispered against his heated skin:

'Barbarian!'

'No. You belong to me, which is why you hated me so much at the beginning.'

Driven by his own demon, he suddenly swung her up into his arms, cradling her trembling body, and moving back through the secret shadowed night into the purple jungle. The moonlight glanced across his dark face; the arrogant nose and the high cheekbones, the deeply cleft chin. Deborah found herself gripping both of her arms behind his head, shaking with nervous intensity. It was intolerable to be so isolated, and fabulous too. Intolerable to want so much yet be afraid.

Under the canopy of palms he lowered her to the bank, bending her backwards and leaning over her. 'You *are* mine, aren't you?'

She covered her eyes with a white hand, her hair spilling backwards. 'It would be much better to hate you!'

'No.'

'You can have any woman you like. Just pick one out.'

'I already have!' he said, trapping her hand and lifting it away. 'None of them stand a chance against you. I decided that right away.'

Deborah could only stare up at him, almost drugged with sensation. 'I never expected ... I never wanted any of this to happen!' she whispered to him, consumed by a contradictory need to deny her own feelings. She wasn't brave and just the touch of his hand made her blood thunder in her ears.

Cal gave a brief muffled exclamation, his silver eyes blazing, then he half-lifted her and held her back against his arm. 'Just don't waste time trying to run away from me!'

It was a warning, not in the least tender, and it flicked at her like a whip. She felt bound and helpless, exposed for the first time in her sheltered young life to the fire of sensuality, so fierce and so leaping that it defeated all normal control. It was like being sealed off in a blazing world of the senses while she lay rapt in the half-circle of his arm, her skin burning to his touch but drawing him irresistibly. He was the possessor, she was the possessed, and it was the most intimate encounter she had ever known in her life.

'Please, *no*!' she said, staying his caressing hand. 'You know how you make me feel!'

'I know I want you to be a good, sweet little girl just

as much as you do, but you're making it too damned hard!'

'No!' she said again, and turned her head into his hard chest.

'Are you begging?'

'Yes!'

'Just words, my love, and I can disprove them. Your heart is racing so wildly. You're such a fastidious, beautiful girl and your mouth tastes exquisite. Stop trembling, Deborah, I know this is all unknown to you. You're even making it new to me, the texture of a woman's skin, the delicate contours of her body. All the spellbinding things that can mean everything or nothing!'

It was frightening, the delight he gave her as his hand touched the creamy skin of her nape and slid round under her chin, lifting her head to him again. 'I won't touch you if you don't want me to!'

She made a small sound of pain and his eyes narrowed.

'Some time soon I'm going to be your lover. Not tonight, but soon. For the first time in my life I know what hell it is to want a woman!'

'*Do* you? Do you want me?' Recklessly she lifted herself up to him, a flame running through her and a witchcraft she didn't know she possessed.

Some alien light flared in his eyes and he dragged his hand through her curls, the tight control he had on himself snapping. 'You said I couldn't make you cry!'

Belatedly she realised the driving male force in him, the strength and the power. He had her pinned beside him, the world on fire, using his strength deliberately, covering her creamy vulnerable face and throat with a track of kisses, his hand curved in possession over her breast as his heart stormed into her own. She could take no more and the tears began swiftly falling. They slid softly down her cheek and came into his mouth, and he put a finger to one glittering drop and put her away from him.

'If it makes you feel any better, I ache for you!'

She lay on the cushiony sand almost dazzled. 'I'm sorry. You've no idea how sorry I am!'

His glance glittered over her from head to toe. 'I've always prided myself on my control, but I guess there's got to be the woman who can make you forget it. And now you know I want you, and one more thing—I'm not going to wait very much longer!'

'I can't hear what you're saying,' she said, wanting his tenderness but knowing that at that moment she wouldn't get it. Cal seemed angry with both of them. 'I can't go back to the house!' She broke off, her voice quivering.

'Why not? Because it's fairly obvious you've been made love to with passion?'

'Yes.' She let out her breath on a long, shuddering sigh.

'Then maybe it's a good idea!' Cal pulled her swaying to her feet, holding her steady with bruising strength.

'No, *Tom* ...' she said with a faint hysteria.

'What's Tom got to do with it?'

'It would hurt him.'

'How?' he bit out curtly.

'I don't know!'

He shook her until her curls tumbled around her face in silken disorder, then inexplicably he gathered her up against him with a protectiveness that astounded her. 'You leave Tom to me.'

'I've only just come into Tommy's life. I can't walk out of it!'

'Oh yes. you can, and you will. I won't have him mistaking you for someone else. You're Deborah, not Beth, and you belong to me!'

'Not yet!' she said with a drowsy resistance. 'Maybe not ever.'

'We'll see about that,' he returned grimly. 'Tom is my

friend and I feel for him. I don't want to see him lose out either, and you'll only hurt him!'

'How can I?' She closed her teeth on her trembling bottom lip that pulsed from the hard touch of his mouth.

'All this afternoon and tonight, from the minute we arrived, he never got tired of looking at you. I don't blame him, and I bore it because you're unconsciously very provoking, but the whole situation can only hurt him. Can't you see that?'

'I can't believe it,' she said.

'Then you're a fool. He's in love with you!'

'You must be going crazy!' she said, furious now and ready to over-react.

'I know Tom better than you do. In fact what you know about men could be written on a pin's head. Even my grandfather's not safe from you!'

She hit him then, as hard as she knew how, with her strong pianist's fingers, losing her head completely and startling herself with the feeling that spilled out of her, the arousal Cal himself had evoked. Her head tilted back without fear, even though a sliver of moonlight showed the expression on his face.

'Don't ever do that again or your ravishment will be untimely!' He jerked her to him and held her with a cruel grip. 'Now we're going to walk back up to the house!'

'No, I'm not!' she said, gritting her teeth.

'You only think you know me, Deborah,' he warned softly. 'If you choose to act like a little wildcat then you deserve what you get!'

'Did I deserve all this, tell me? I think I've got bruises all over me!'

'Good. That way you won't mistake me for anyone else. You need a little mastering once you get going. I've always suspected it.'

'I must have a genius for self-destruction, going with you!' she said on a protest.

'You've a genius for self-destruction all right, but I'm the one to save you. Don't pretend you're not a part of me. You've betrayed yourself very well!'

'I'm not worried. Women must do that all the time with you!' she said much too rashly, for careless and mocking, within full view of the house, he turned her into his arms and dropped a hard punishing kiss on her mouth with an audience of two. It seemed brutal to Deborah, but then Cal was very cruel and she didn't know what to do about it.

# CHAPTER EIGHT

THEY called a truce until after Christmas Day, because neither of them wanted to cast the slightest shadow on that festive day or lessen the household's enjoyment of it. Deborah even held up her cheek for the merest glancing brush of Cal's mouth as he presented her with a beautiful Chinese necklace cut from a single piece of jade. His grandfather's gift was a branch of coral carved into an exquisite statuette, and Tom's a superb handbag and matching shoes from Italy. Chris received a fine watch suitable to his years, a veritable fleet of larger scale Corgi cars, new clothes, a tennis racquet together with John Newcombe's latest book, and a model of a Superfortress to put together. Deborah and Chris felt their own gifts very modest in comparison, but they were received by all three men with a great show that they were the very thing they had been wanting; the old man was so gracious as to put on his shirt and classic cravat, looking very spare and dashing.

The day passed in a blue and golden dream, with luncheon at the compound and dinner at the hotel that evening as a kind of goodwill gesture which was obviously appreciated by the guests, for they all stood up and clapped when the old man walked in with his party, while he responded with a courtly, humorous wave of his hand like their own kind of royalty.

Boxing day proved another matter. Cal suggested exploring the coral beds halfway through the morning, when a call from the hotel receptionist informed them that a Mrs Eve Mangan and her daughter had come in on the early launch from the mainland and were in fact already on their way up to the compound in the hotel jeep. The old man took this rather better than his grandson was expecting, reasoning perhaps that they had had a perfect trouble-free day yesterday, so that by the time Eve and Marisa swept in, they were all assembled on the terrace with a round of cold drinks.

'Hello there!' Eve came up the stairs, studying their downbent faces that bit uncertainly. She had nearly expected to find the massive wrought-iron gates locked to them, knowing the old man's occasional eccentricities, so it was exhilarating to see them all smiling. She was absolutely furious with Tom, though she kept the fact well hidden as she kissed him. Deborah, who was shaking back her glorious hair, her young, slender body shown to great advantage in a brief halter and matching shorts, she could cheerfully have shoved off the balcony, but caution filled her mind.

The old man played the gracious host, holding her chair. 'Do sit down, Eve. Marisa, how are you, my dear? You always look very fetching. The season's greeting to both of you. Such a surprise to see you here on the island, Eve. I thought you had other plans?'

'We did intend to jet off somewhere,' Eve said offhandedly, sinking into the wicker chair and fanning her perfect, lightly made-up skin, 'but then I got so lonesome for Tom. He wanted to stay with me, of course, but I packed him off. I know how devoted he is to you all. Deborah!' Eve turned her glossy black head, 'how charming you look. Yellow is definitely your colour—but no tan? I should be like a native by now. Where is young Christopher, by the way?'

'Practising his serve, I think!' Deborah said pleasantly. 'Tommy gave him a racquet for Christmas.'

'Did you, Tom? How nice. Exercise is always very good for children.'

Marisa, in her favourite hot pink, was busy accepting a long frosted drink from Cal, devouring him with her dark, melting eyes. 'Hi there, stranger! Remember me?'

'Naturally!' he said idly. 'Just curl up there and drink that.' He glanced towards Deborah. 'Having one?'

'No, thank you!'

Eve's shapely nose was just brushing the mint. 'Delicious! I felt somewhat uncomfortable intruding on you all.'

'How could you?' Cal responded, bowing very slightly. 'How did your Christmas go?'

'We spent it with the Dawsons and a few of their friends, then at the last minute I decided to come across here. It's heavenly, isn't it? I've always loved the island.'

'You'll have lunch with us, of course?' the old man said. Eve smiled.

'Why, we'd love to if you're sure it's not interfering with your plans!'

'Robert was just going to show Deborah the coral gardens.'

'Hasn't she seen them yet?' Eve enquired, opening up her large dark eyes.

'Not from under the water, which is absolutely the best way to see them.'

'Can't I come too?' Marisa asked, pouting like a kitten.

Cal hesitated fractionally and Deborah issued the invitation. 'Why, of course. Have you a swimsuit?'

'Underneath. You're taller than I am, in any case!'

'And slimmer,' Tom said unexpectedly.

Marisa's pout became more pronounced. 'All of us indulge over Christmas, T.J.'

'No news!' he said, and laughed, patting his own taut frame.

'Well, I'll have a rest before lunch,' the old man said. 'We had a very stimulating night up at the hotel, so if you and Tom want to have a chat, Eve?' he suggested tactfully.

'That will be lovely!' Eve said, and smiled blissfully and quite falsely at Tom. She hadn't slept at all this last week since their violent disagreement, and from the expression in the depths of his eyes he hadn't forgotten. Coming here like this had almost made her feel cheap. She was a fool to throw herself at him, but she needed him badly and the thought that she was losing him shocked her.

He didn't like to be treated possessively. He didn't even love her, she knew that, but they got on well together and were sexually suited. He had the upper hand because his feelings were far less intense, and perversely this tied her to him. Her husband, Dennis, Eve had despised, although he had been a very kind and unselfish man, considering her always because he was a gentleman and not the miserable worm she had sometimes thought and even called him. Tom could dispense with her at any time, and since the girl Deborah had appeared on the scene she had been forced face to face with this knowledge. So powerful was her jealousy that if the girl had been drowning she wouldn't have lifted a finger to rescue her. Neither would Marisa, Eve counted on that, but in that she was wrong, for Marisa had a little of her father in her and murderous feelings were never easy to live with.

By the time the old man had retired to his room in the east wing and Cal and the girls had gone down to the beach, Eve had determined to have it out with Tom. Not like the last time, when she had gripped her hands together so that she wouldn't hurl something at him, but quietly, sympathetically, playing on their friendship and what they had meant to each other.

'You know I've missed you, darling!' she turned her head to look out over the blue lagoon. 'Give me your hand.'

He reached out and touched her fingers. 'I should apologise for that last time.'

'Both of us were to blame. You know how important you are to me, Tom. You can't blame me for being jealous of anyone you want to spend your time with. But, Tom dearest, who is going to come first?'

'I have a duty to Deborah and young Christopher,' he replied, 'a sacred duty. I've never said this to anyone before, but Beth, their mother, was the only woman I've ever loved. I mean *really* loved, as a man should love a woman. With passion and tenderness and a longing to cherish.'

Eve's angry eyes filled with real tears. She was unbelievably stricken. There was no mistaking the sincerity of his tone, the expression in his dark eyes. 'How cruel men can be!' she said sightlessly, daring the tears to fall and ruin her mascara.

'I'm sorry, my dear,' Tom said gently, 'I don't want to hurt you. I like you very much, but never at any moment of our relationship have I said I loved you.'

'No, you just took all you could get!' she said bitterly, an ugly flush in her cheeks.

'Maybe I did, but it was given very freely. We're adult people. Both of us were lonely. I thought we were fulfilling a mutual need!'

'I love you, Tom!' she said harshly. 'Give me a cigarette.'

'I haven't got one on me, but I can get you some.'

'No, sit down. Just tell me this and be completely honest. If this girl hadn't come into your life, would you have married me?'

'I don't understand what you're talking about!'

His tone should have silenced Eve, but it didn't. 'This Deborah!' she said, and almost screeched.

'Deborah was entrusted to me by her mother. She's just twenty years old, or she soon will be. Young enough to be my daughter.'

'That doesn't stop you loving her!'

'No, it doesn't,' he returned quite calmly, thereby administering a deadly blow.

'So you admit it?' she hissed at him, her black eyes flashing. 'You poor deluded fool! She sees you as a beloved older brother!'

'And that means enough to me,' he returned steadily.

'I'll tell her. I'll tell the old man. He won't stand for it!' Her full mouth began to work.

Tom looked at her and saw for the first time the depths of her jealousy, and was sickened and sorry. He was to blame for a lot. 'Don't do this to yourself, Eve,' he said gently. 'I'm only Deb's temporary guardian. She'll marry one day. She's so beautiful that some man's going to claim her.'

'Are you telling me that things will go on as they are?' She stared at him incredulously.

'Deborah will never hear from me that I love her, and she'll never suspect it. I care far too much about her to hurt her in any way. In so many ways she's Beth all over again. It's difficult to explain.'

'You'd better do it to a psychiatrist!' Eve said violently. 'Don't imagine he'll believe in the purity of your motives!'

'You know, if you say anything to Deborah this is the end of us.'

'It's the end of us anyway, isn't it?' she demanded. 'The girl's like a time bomb in our midst. She's wrecking all my dreams!'

'Oh, come now, Eve, you're a mature woman, a very attractive woman. You could remarry tomorrow if you wanted to. Grant Ormiston has been in love with you for years!'

'For some damned silly reason I'm in love with you,' she said bitterly, 'and I'm at breaking point. Why should this girl come into our lives and change everything? I *hate* her!'

'She didn't change anything, Eve,' Tom said quietly.

'You may have been planning on marriage, but in not marrying you I don't think I'm failing you. We were an unlikely team. You wanted it right from the beginning. You "lost" yourself with me that very first weekend— you got me fairly in your sights and that was it. I'm grateful to you for all the good times we've had, but I didn't know there was an obligation to marry you.'

Eve's mouth framed an ugly word. 'So that's it! The search isn't over. Nothing in my life has gone according to plan!'

'Whose life does? You could call me the all-time loser!'

'I bleed for you, you poor suffering soul! Really this is the classic situation, isn't it, the middle-aged man falling for a young girl?'

Tom stiffened. 'Leave Deborah out of it! I've never hit a woman in my life, but if you don't keep your voice down ...'

'I don't care if you hit me or not. She's a conniving little bitch, but it's not you she's after!'

'That's the only sensible thing you've said. When Deborah marries the man she truly loves I'll be happy for her. I'll even give her away. Her well-being is very precious to me, and I've come to love young Chris too. I believe both of them care about me and you're not going to upset anything with your wild allegations, and never here in front of my friends. Your daughter wouldn't thank you for it. Why don't you begin to consider her?'

'Don't preach to me, Tom. I know your darkest secret.'

His rugged face hardened. 'If it were only me you could hurt I wouldn't care if you shouted it from the rooftops, but you won't hurt Deborah!' He looked away from her, torn between disgust and pity so that he didn't know what struck him. Pain splintered across his head and he went down like a stone, falling sideways out of the chair and sprawling on the geometric tiles. Eve stood over him for an interminable minute, then she turned around in full flight, hurling herself down the stairs and out to the waiting jeep. The swine had deceived her and she didn't care if he was dead!

Brilliant ribbons of little coloured fish flashed through the water, playing hide and seek in among the hanging gardens. Enthralled, Deborah swam along the coral pinnacles and spires that threw shadows over the brilliantly clear water, lit with the palest blue light. It was incredibly beautiful underwater, an exquisite silent world full of multi-colours. The coral labyrinths were fantastic, fragrant and delicate or massive, weighing many tons; the golden leaf and the great colonies of staghorns, the flange and the brain corals, the flamboyant red gorgonia and the Icis, the organ pipe corals and the beautiful chrysanthemums in a flowering fantasy of delicate pastels.

It was fascinating and everywhere the little jewel-coloured fish flitted up as Deborah dived deeper or whirled round to join her. An invader she might have been in the perfect fantasia, but they didn't seem to mind in the least; indeed they were friendly, even the dignified dowagers, the fat coral trout. She stared from a distance at the Tridacnas, the giant clams, and the carnivorous anemones that housed fleets of gaily-coloured little guard fish, a bright scarlet with white cross-bands.

Beneath her she could see Cal swimming with strong graceful strokes, rolling away now for a dive along a deeper ravine. A cloud of demoiselles, the gorgeous violet-blue little tropical fish, flashed out of the sculptured coral barriers, the trees and the shrubs and the flowers, the great silent cathedrals, to circle her and stare at her avidly, not even bothering to move out of her way. Beautiful as the corals had been seen from the boat or fossicking at low tide, it was nothing compared to this.

The water rippled around her as Marisa drifted by, as absorbed as she was, but the water remained brilliantly clear, the sunlight piercing the gaps in the reef and showing the glittering sand at the bottom. It was an experience she could never have missed, an enchantment and a source of great wonder. A Red Emperor, easily three feet long and one of the best eating fish on the reef, flashed after a little zebra angel, all electric blue and yellow stripes, but lost it to a spreading dusky pink anemone. Deborah could spend days drifting like this with her face mask and snorkel. It was so beautiful, so awesome, the coral so intricately fashioned that it was nearly impossible to remember many sailing ships had been wrecked on reefs like this. The great wall of coral that formed the Great Barrier stretched almost continuously for over twelve hundred miles. In the days of sail it had struck fear into seamen, and even today the great ocean-going liners approached it with great caution. Many ships had been wrecked on the reef, many more driven on to it by cyclones, even Spanish and Portuguese galleons had perhaps spilled treasure on to the ocean floor. This was the world's finest storehouse of coral and housed every kind of coral known to marine biology, a petrified multi-hued forest, and so incredibly exotic that Deborah couldn't see enough of it.

A minute later Cal swam back into sight, preceded by a small fleet of harlequin fish and the yellow butterfly cod. He pointed decisively to the surface and swam towards her. This was the signal to kick to the top before their air ran out. Deborah looked round once more at this magical world, then began to kick strongly towards the sunlight, surfacing almost beside Cal, and a few seconds later, Marisa. Cal pulled off his mask and smiled at them.

'Well?'

'Fantastic!' said Deborah. 'I'm going to do it again!'

'I thought you might, but not today. I promised Chris I would take him over to Lunar Cay to see all the bird life. If you feel all right we'll swim in. Both of you keep alongside me!'

Exhilarated, Deborah pulled ahead, but by the time

Cal reached the beach both girls were still coming. He grinned broadly at them. 'Take it easy, you'll be right out of breath!'

'I'm that already!' Marisa said, moving awkwardly in her flippers.

'Here, I'll take those off for you.' Cal bent to help her and Deborah watched them. Marisa's petite but curvy little figure was very adequately displayed in the briefest of black and white bikinis, her well-shaped head sleek and wet, her small foot in Cal's hand. She was eyeing him appealingly, and Deborah couldn't blame her. He looked devastatingly attractive, his lean powerful body, taut and disciplined, burned a deep bronze, his light eyes glittering in his darkly vivid face. It was clear that Marisa found him exciting, for her reactions were unmistakable. She was looking up at him with considerable provocation, her dark eyes frankly sensuous, her small golden breasts almost completely revealed as she leaned on his shoulder. Surprisingly he didn't bat an eyelid, though Deborah felt somewhat uncomfortable although she was arrayed in a more decent two-piece.

The coral sand was a glittering bone-white, the lagoon an incredible blue, transparently green in the shallows, and the great palms and the pandanus feathering the beach threw sharply etched shadows. It was Paradise unspoiled and utterly fascinating.

Suddenly, for no apparent reason, Deborah felt a chill through her body, a weight of anxiety that came from nowhere and had no place in such a breathtaking world. She looked back towards the house and a flicker of premonition crossed her face.

'What is it?' Cal asked abruptly, gripping her shoulder.

'I don't know!' She turned to look up at him. 'Something's wrong!'

'Oh, really,' Marisa laughed faintly maliciously, 'you must have a touch of the deeps!'

Cal's gaze was pinned on Deborah's face. He was frowning and his white teeth snapped together. 'You haven't got a headache, have you?'

'No.' Her heart was beginning to beat faster and her first thoughts of Christopher seemed to ease. 'Something's wrong at the house. I'm going up!'

'Let her!' Marisa chimed in, exhibiting her resentment. 'Stay here with me, Cal. This is heaven!'

Deborah left her gear lying on the sand. She turned and fled across the beach, not pausing even though she heard Cal call after her. By the time she reached the lower terrace she was breathless and Cal was beside her, his breathing undisturbed, his eyes sparkling with a faint anger and puzziement. 'You'll kill yourself racing about like this in the heat. You've gone very pale. What *is* it? Has Marisa upset you? Or Eve?'

'Of course not!'

'Then damn it, what is it? Can't you talk to me?'

'I've just got this strange feeling,' she panted.

'That's obvious to see!'

The old man came to the balcony, looked over it, and saw them standing so close together, Cal pinning her wrist. 'Tom's had a fall!' he called to them. 'He's all right, but you'd better come up!'

'Good God!' Cal looked from his grandfather's grim face, then intently back to Deborah. 'Take it easy now.'

'I knew something was wrong!' she said in a panic, and the tears stood in her eyes.

'He's all right. The old man's infallible!' His lean brown fingers twined through her own and he half-pulled her up the short flight of steps, his forehead pleating as they came level with the old man. 'What happened?'

Robert McGovern hesitated. 'Well, I suppose you have to know. It appears that Eve clobbered him!'

'Oh, no!'

'Sit down.' Cal pushed the girl gently into a chair.

'What for?' He looked back at his grandfather.

'Search me. A lovers' tiff, perhaps!'

'Where is he now?'

'Lying down. I found him and poor old Lee fetched me up from the floor. It gave me quite a shock. I don't usually see Tom decorating the tiles. He has a lump on the side of his head the size of a duck egg.'

'It must be aching very badly,' Deborah said in a low, anguished voice.

'He'll live,' the old man reassured her. 'I've always maintained that Boxing Day is well named! Don't upset yourself, child. A good rest is all Tom needs. He's a wee bit shaken, but all right. The doctor is coming over from the hotel. I'd say that wound needs a stitch or two.'

'Are *you* all right?' Cal asked, studying his grandfather intently.

'Sure I am! Don't fuss now!'

'Where's Eve?'

'Really I don't know. Either sending out for reinforcements or barricading herself up in her hotel room. How glad I am that I'm too old for tender feuds!'

'Why should she do it?' Deborah asked jaggedly, reaching out and touching the old man's hand to draw him down into a chair beside her.

He grinned. 'You know the old story ... hell hath no fury! I'm very much afraid it's true.'

'There are smarter ways of jollying a man along!' Cal said, exasperated. 'This leaves us in a very odd position. Should we throw Eve off the island?'

'I'll leave the matter to you,' his grandfather answered.

'Quite possibly I might have to take that line!'

Marisa came up from the garden and joined them, alerted by their expressions and the set of their bodies, in no way relaxed. 'What happened? What's the matter?'

'Tom's had an accident,' the old man said a shade tersely.

'Oh, how dreadful! Is he all right?'

'Yes,' the old man responded, warming slightly to her obvious sincerity. 'Just a nasty knock, bleeding and so forth.'

'How very odd! Deborah thought there was something wrong at the house. She must be psychic!'

Cal shrugged his wide shoulders, his silver eyes brooding. 'I always thought she was different from other girls.'

'May I see him?' Deborah asked.

'I imagine he'd like that,' the old man patted her hands.

'I'll go with you,' Cal said shortly, 'but we'll change first. Poor old Tom, if that doesn't beat everything. We've been in the ring all year, and now this! A man's not safe on a tropic island.'

At this point Marisa looked all about for her mother or any sign of the jeep, but she didn't ask questions and merely went swiftly to change into her clothes. She had thought her mother strung up, but my, oh my, what had she done?


They found Tom propped up in bed with a very professional-looking bandage round his head. He was smiling ruefully, but there was a distinct pallor under his tan that betrayed his shock.

'Tommy!' Deborah went to him, her face full of loving concern.

'It's all right, baby, it's nothing. I guess I deserved it.'

'Care to tell us what happened?' Cal pulled up a chair for Deborah, who had perched herself on the bed, as delicate as a dryad in her flimsy little sundress.

Tom seemed to inhale a large quantity of air. 'Eve and I exchanged a few pertinent words.'

'Damn!' said Cal.

'I'm sorry, old man, I can't marry her for the good of the firm.'

'I never mentioned the word!'

'*She* did!' Tom disclosed ruefully.

'Women are like that.'

'All right, I'm sorry. Maybe I've been a cad.'

'Just because you don't want to marry her?' Deborah demanded incredulously.

'Maybe Tom led her to believe he would,' Cal said dryly.

Tom shook his head gingerly. 'I don't think so. It wouldn't have done either of us any good. I'm damned sorry—Eve's a very attractive woman and we've had some good times together. I didn't want her to suffer on my account, or lose her dignity.'

'Is your head hurting badly?' Deborah asked, her green eyes brilliant with compassion.

'Not too much. But my pride! That's something else again. To be floored by a woman! It's Bob I'm worried about. He found me lying in a pool of blood, and he's not a young man any more.'

'And certainly he prefers to see you enjoying yourself. Ah well,' Cal threw back his head abruptly, 'what happens now? Have you both done, or can we expect a rematch?'

'Don't mention it.' Tom actually shuddered.

Cal looked up. 'Yes, Lee, what is it?'

Lee, the Chinest manservant, had come to the door, for once wide-eyed, his voice almost excited. 'The doctor has arrived, Mr Robert. Shall I show him in?'

'Well yes, of course. Deborah, why don't you go out into the air for a few minutes? You look very pale. I'll stay here with Tom.'

'Yes, go, Deb!' Tom urged her, the wry smile still on his face. 'For all my brave show I could still turn chicken.'

'The blood is coming through the bandage,' she said almost fearfully, her green eyes enormous.

'It's a wonder it didn't split open like a melon!'

'Out!' Cal ordered her as she began to swallow. 'This

is limited to men only. Go back to my grandfather and see if he's all right.'

'What about Marisa?' she asked him. 'She'll be very upset about her mother.'

'Small wonder!' he rejoined, as arrogant as the devil. 'I don't like it myself. Leave it to me, I'll do everything that has to be done. You've never mentioned it, Tom, but are you given to fainting?'

'Oh, shut up!' Tom said wearily, and shut his eyes. 'Stitches just depress me, that's all!'

'I'll come back,' Deborah promised sweetly, still hovering in the doorway.

'Not until you're called,' Cal tacked on emphatically.

The doctor, a tanned, very pleasant-looking man in his early fifties, was swinging along the parquet corridor. Deborah smiled at him in passing, then went through the house to see if there was anything she could do for Cal's grandfather. She felt a sudden spurt of pity for Marisa but none for Eve. Her own clash with Eve had appalled her, and why she should come here to the Mc-Govern compound and start something like this was beyond her. Couldn't she have waited for a more private place to get livid with Tom? She still didn't know what Eve had hit him with, but it must have been something to hand; a heavy ashtray or a pot plant. It seemed a very violent reaction, but of course Eve was violent. Cal would have to tell Marisa, but for her own sake Deborah didn't want to see the girl.

As it happened she didn't have to; the old man, long used to disasters and a law to himself on the island, had already broken the news to Marisa and made arrangements for her to be taken back to the hotel. She didn't wish to stay, being understandably upset and embarrassed.

Tom felt he had a lot to say after the doctor had gone. He didn't particularly want to, but he had been warned.

Cal had always been easy to talk to and he remained calm and unsurprised when Tom pointed out his anxieties on Deborah's behalf: Eve had a tongue on her, and now that she considered herself bitterly rejected she could prove vicious. Cal turned away from the open window and spoke very quietly, though his eyes glinted:

'Then I'll just have to speak to her, won't I?'

'What would you say?'

'That I intend to marry Deborah, and should she decide to indulge in vindictive gossip or create a minor scandal she'll be very sorry!'

Tom half got up off the bed, his rugged face blank. 'Excuse me a moment, what was that you said?'

'Oughtn't you lie down?' Cal said firmly.

'In a minute. I particularly want to get this right.'

'I said I intend to marry Deborah. I shouldn't worry about it, Tom. I'll look after her very well!'

Tom raised a hand to his injured head, his dark eyes suffering. 'I take it she's in love with you?'

The younger man considered him for a moment compassionately. 'I think she knows very little about men and love, Tom, except her love for her family, which includes you!'

'Well, well!' Tom pulled back his shoulders and stared away out of the window. 'Knowing the speed at which you move I shouldn't be stunned, but I am. I want to say it's great news, but I feel I've lost them all at once.'

Cal turned and looked at him. 'Come on now, you'll be seeing so much of us all that you'll hardly have your home to yourself!'

Tom didn't answer for a minute. He stood up, said 'Damn!' then sank on to the bed again, gritting his teeth. 'Well, Deb's an extraordinary girl and you're an extraordinary man. I suppose it's absolutely perfect. I just didn't realise. God, you're a fast worker!'

'Is it all right with you?' Cal held his glance squarely.

'Splendid. I just expected to lose her gradually, not all at once. Did I ever tell you how much I loved her mother?'

'No, not really,' Cal smiled at him, 'but it sort of shows. Almost any man could love Deborah. If Big Bob was forty—no, thirty years younger, I'm sure he'd run off with her right under both our noses!'

Tom was frowning, still rather dazed. 'And you love her?'

'That's a very stupid question, Tom. Some men only realise what they've got when they lose it, but I know what I've got now. Eventually Deborah will have a very big job on her hands, and I know she can do it.'

At this Tom sighed, then he started to grin. 'You McGoverns! You see everything against how it will affect the business!'

'Well, I could hardly marry a very stupid, dull girl!' Cal pointed out smoothly.

'You could marry anyone you liked!'

'All I want is Deborah, and I know I can make her happy. Of course there's going to be the time she's up in the air about something and there's someone she wants to talk to, and there'll always be you. Chris is counting on his Uncle Tom.'

'Yes, I think he cares for me,' Tom said in a comforted way.

'They both do! I'm afraid it would upset them if you don't give me your blessing.'

'You've got it,' Tom said slowly. 'God, Cal, you know you've got it. I'm just finding it hard to take it all in. Maybe it's the blow on the head. The lord knows there's no man I trust more than you, unless it's Bob. It's just the sense of ... loss, I suppose you'd call it. The unexpectedness of the whole business. You understand?'

'Not loss, Tom,' Cal pointed out gently, 'gain. We've always regarded you as a close friend. Now you'll be gaining a family as well. I'm afraid I might have to have a word with Eve, though!'

'Well, yes.' Tom considered. 'Her attitude to Deb is downright peculiar. She hates her.'

'That's a pity!' Cal said grimly. 'It's rather important to me that everyone should love and admire her. Are you absolutely certain it's all over between you and Eve?'

Tom looked back at him solemnly. 'I feel I never want to lay eyes on her again, which makes a mockery of our friendship. Bogus all through. I feel kind of contemptible and Eve's in a very nasty mood, that's why I told you.'

The sunlight slanting across the room emphasised Cal's darkly formidable look. 'If she tries to sling any mud around she'll only get hurt,' he said, deadly quiet.

Tom stared up at him for a moment. 'I wouldn't care to cross you myself. You know you're very much like Bob?'

'I expect that's it, then!' Cal's expression lightened and he smiled back at the other man. 'You know Marisa comes in for her share of Denn's estate at the end of next month? It would be a good thing if she took a trip around the world, got away from her mother. Eve has never been good for her.'

Tom heaved a sigh and touched his head irritably because it was paining him. 'I've always been fond of Marisa and I must admit that's true. Why Eve imagines I'm the only person in the world she really cares about I don't know. I've been level with her all along. She made the play for me, and that's in the strictest confidence. Now it's over and there's nothing left, I guess I'm glad. I'm complete bachelor material!'

'From what I've seen you're probably better off,' Cal rejoined suavely. 'Anyway, you're excellent uncle material. Don't worry, Tom, we'll continue as well as we've ever done. You've played a very important part in all this. You brought Deborah into my life!'

Tom glanced up at him, looking surprisingly better. 'I feel that *is* important. If she has to marry anyone I prefer it to be you. I've had my moment of self-pity and it hurt like the old days all over again, but it has nothing to do with Deb. She's young. She's the future, and I'm going to be around for the boy. Naturally I wish to educate him and fulfil my obligations to Beth.'

'There's nothing I'd want better. You look a bit worn, Tom,' Cal said briskly, 'have a rest. I suppose it's a miracle you're still alive. That was a damned heavy thing she hit you with!'

'Yes,' Tom said with great conviction, 'and a splendid aim. I never saw it coming. We were both pretty steamed up, and I guess she just lost her head.'

'Well, I'm glad we didn't have any pokers around. It's wise not to look away from a woman when she's in that kind of mood. One's not really dealing with the full deck. Now I think I'll take a stroll over to the hotel.'

'Gently, Cal, gently,' Tom warned him warily. 'She wouldn't spare you a blatant scene in her present mood!'

There was derision in Cal's sparkling light eyes. 'I'm not open to hurt or ridicule or anything else from Eve Mangan. I dislike using the whip hand, but I've got it. I could make a lot of unpleasant things happen to Eve's investments, but I'm going to hold to the happy view that she won't want to do or say anything to hurt any of us. After all, Deborah has done nothing to harm her, except perhaps just be herself. It's easier to accuse someone else than expose yourself or take the blame. Perhaps Eve will want to renew her friendship with Ormiston; it's not unusual. She might even get mad enough to marry him. I hope she does now, for Marisa's sake. Marisa's too old to act the schoolgirl tied to her mother's apron strings. The money might change everything. It wasn't a great deal when we talk about real money, but it should be enough!'

'Yes,' Tom nodded, 'it's quite possible it will be, but I'd like to point out at this point that Marisa has always had her heart set on you!'

'Quite so,' Cal murmured cynically, 'Marisa and a few others. It's grand to be popular and I'm not exactly poor. Women find money extremely reassuring!'

'Hah!' Tom bit back a laugh. 'You wouldn't have the slightest bother if you were out on the dole. There would always be some beautiful girl anxious to support you.'

'How unlikely! Some men might find it enjoyable, but I take my pleasures from different things.'

'And we're very proud of you,' Tom saluted him mockingly. 'I can see a knighthood and all sorts of things coming up.'

Cal laughed and moved to the door with his vital, swinging movements. 'I won't accept it for years yet. Rest easy, Tom, everything will be all right. By the way, I was taking Deborah and Chris over to Lunar Cay this afternoon, but we'll wait until you're better. Perhaps to-morrow!'

'Yes, I wish you would,' Tom said seriously. 'I'd like to be there.'

'Then it's all arranged. See you, pal—now for my discussion with your ex-lady-friend!'

Tom moaned out loud, his rangy body expressive. 'I suppose you must take a stand, and God help me, I'm nearly out cold!'

'Pretty much,' Cal agreed gently, and snapped the door shut. He didn't anticipate any real scenes. Eve might have played herself out, and in any case, she wouldn't be stupid enough to involve any one of them for some kind of revenge. He would make it impossible for her. Deborah would marry him and he knew how to look after his own and preserve the McGovern name. Was there anyone who at some stage of their lives didn't make a fool of themselves? Eve would be sensible. It was the only way, and even if it took her the whole wretched day, she would see it his way and make a graceful exit. Cal was absolutely determined to protect every one of them, and he would marry Deborah even if she furiously resisted.

As it happened, Eve was in a very ugly mood, enhanced by a few brandies and a scene with her daughter, who for once in her life had actually spoken out, declaring herself shamed and mortified both by her mother's uncontrolled behaviour and by the things she was threatening while she was submerged by her jealous rage. Marisa was genuinely fond of Tom, and she shied away completely from angering the McGoverns. Tom's two orphans she couldn't care less about, but she had the dismal notion that the old man would protect them to the hilt.

Their short, violent scene sent Marisa, with a throbbing head, into the hotel pool where she was taken up almost at once by a young group, one of whom knew her quite well. She had wanted to be alone, but that proved impossible, and after a while under the spell of their easy chatter and some frank male appreciation she began to feel better.

One of the girls was speaking about her coming trip to Europe, and Marisa considered that were it not for Cal she would head off herself. She had waited a long time for her inheritance and it would buy her freedom. Having never worked a day in her life, she had at no time considered a job; it seemed a lot easier to stay with Eve, who made her a very adequate allowance. They both dressed beautifully and were known for it. Eve had never been stingy with money, just her love and her time.

Now Marisa felt sickened when she remembered Eve's stream of threats. She seemed bent on slandering Tom's reputation and with him the girl's. Poor Tom! He didn't deserve it, for he was a very nice man. Marisa had known all along that her mother had got in too deep with Tom. Tom was a strange one in his way, tough and tender, and his heart had been given once and a long time ago. Very likely, had he been more malleable and danced attendance on Eve, she would have tired of him, for that was her way.

Remaining at the pool and later having the poolside smörgasbord luncheon with the rest of the group, Marisa had no knowledge of Cal McGovern's visit. She only knew that from that day on and quite inexplicably, for Eve had threatened violence on all their heads and the spreading of a few ugly rumours about Tom Reynolds and his ward, Eve turned notoriously tight-lipped about her break-up with Tom. It was Grant Ormiston's turn to swing back into favour, which he did, while Eve convinced herself that Tom no longer meant anything to her. She continued to look at the peak of her powers, impeccably groomed, which was what really counted.

# CHAPTER NINE

DEBORAH awoke on her birthday morning to the shower of pebbles against the shutters. She lay there for a moment wondering if the noise was part of her dream, then it came again, muffled but urgent, bringing her out of her delicious languor. She snatched up her silk robe and went to the windows, throwing up the insect screen and looking down.

'Cal!' She stretched out a hand to him as if she wanted to touch him when he'd been enormously distant for days.

'Happy birthday!' he said softly. 'You look enchanting in that ruffled thing, but get dressed and come down.'

'But it's only ....' she looked back frantically at the wall clock '... six o'clock!'

'So?'

'I'm afraid I'm not even awake yet!'

'You look pretty wide-eyed to me. Are you coming down or am I coming up?'

'I suppose you would!'

'Count on it! Such is the pull of your fascination.'

'I suppose you've decided to be nice to me on my birthday?'

'*And* our last day on the island for quite a while. Tomorrow I won't have time to relax.'

He stood poised with his black head tilted up, his eyes a sparkling silver, mocking as usual, but very different from the friendly, businesslike treatment of late. He was

175

standing against a great shower of morning glories, the trumpeted blue dawn flower clinging in a cascade to his right shoulder. It was a vivid splash of electric violet rivalling the king jasmine that climbed in a year-round fragrance and profusion of starry white flowers right up to the balconies on that side of the house and had to be cut back to keep it within bounds.

'Oh, to be twenty!' he shook his head as he looked up at her. 'You look a miracle first thing in the morning. I had no idea!'

'Why should you? You hardly know me!'

'Really?' He made a small jeering sound. 'I thought I knew you at a single glance. A revelation. Listen, are you coming?'

'What are we going to do?' she asked.

'Go for a walk. Maybe a swim before breakfast. I'll fetch you up a pearl from the sea bed if you like!'

'That sounds wonderful!'

'Anyway, I'll make absolutely no demands you're not ready to meet!'

'And thank you for that!' Deborah spoke lightly, but the expression on his face and the mockery in his voice brought the rosy colour into her cheeks. She withdrew her bright head and brought down the screen feeling young and lacking in self-assurance but still bent on seeking out the cause of her rising excitement. Cal was a maddening man and he whipped up such a storm in her she scarcely knew what she was doing. Only last night she had convinced herself she was content to let him treat him like a fragile little friend of a friend, but just now, as she looked down at him, it seemed intolerable that he might never want to make love to her again. She needed it, and she couldn't block the thought from her mind, though she was avid to keep her thoughts from him.

Her heart beat very fast as she moved away to brush

her teeth and splash her face with cold water. There was no need to search out an outfit, shorts and a T-shirt would do, or maybe the green and gold Liberty print skirt; most of her beach wear matched up. In the end, feeling a little shy and mindful of Cal's very searching regard, she settled for the skirt and a matching pleated bodice that went with it.

He was waiting for her down in the garden with the butterflies flitting from flower to flower, and saw the vulnerable look about her as well as the elegance and the incredibly fresh young beauty. He seemed to look at her a long time, and her heart gave a convulsive leap. She came up to him rather shyly and he bent his head to brush her smooth scented cheek with his mouth.

'We're the only ones awake!'

'Not for long. Chris gets up at about seven and breakfast is at eight.'

'Don't worry, we'll have completed our business by then!'

Deborah shook back her dark flame-coloured hair, puzzled by the expression on his face. It was vaguely tormenting. 'Why have you been so altered these past days?' she asked him.

'Altered? In what way?'

'You know what I'm talking about.'

'You won't find me much altered, Deborah,' he assured her, and tucked a butterfly orchid delicately shaded in lime green into her hair. 'Once I've made up my mind I never change!'

'And what am I supposed to work out from that?'

He chose to ignore her, his head on one side, considering the effect of the flower in her hair. 'You look very chic. How do those tiny little straps hold your dress up?'

'It's a skirt and top!'

'Oh. Anyway, you look marvellous. Let's walk down

on the beach. It's a celebration of a morning, don't you think? Just right for a birthday.'

She couldn't help smiling as she accepted his helping hand on the climb down. 'Everything smells so sweet. What are all those flowers that have sprung up among the rocks?'

'Storm lilies. They come up like magic after an overnight shower of rain.'

She looked down at the rose-pink bells. 'Everything insists on finding a place for itself, doesn't it? Living, surviving!'

'That's what it's all about!' They had almost reached the beach and Cal turned suddenly, grasping her around her narrow waist and swinging her in a smooth soaring arc through the air before depositing her on the coral sand. All her senses came alive and her limpid green eyes turned brilliant, betraying her. There was some very male challenge about him this morning, a high-tension dynamism that made the adrenalin work in her own body. It was a fantastic feeling to be alone with Cal, for he, in the whole world, had the power to make her come shatteringly alive so that even her skin shivered with the urgency of contact. His hand slid under her chin and lifted her face. Half driven crazy with the need to hide from him, she closed her eyes, and heard his laugh.

'What's this? An invitation?'

'Certainly not!'

'All right, have it your own way.'

She opened her eyes and pulled her head away. 'Which way shall we go?'

'Some faraway beach—perfect for a seduction!'

'*Please!*' She looked back at him for a moment consideringly, conscious of their remoteness.

'Mine, not yours!' he pointed out dryly. 'I just thought I'd head you off. You're an enthralling little witch and you haven't the faintest notion. I'm just worried that I may not be able to deal with the situation.'

'You could deal with any situation,' she said tartly, thinking of Eve Mangan and her early departure—a great anti-climax when she had been expecting some terrible unpleasantness and Tommy had gone very quiet.

'That's nice of you to say that, Deborah, when you've been trying to make a fool of me for days.'

Cal sounded quite serious and she struggled to contradict him. 'I have not! *You're* the one who's been acting the superior family friend. Very condescending!'

'And it hurt you? Good. I went out of my way to do it!'

'But why?'

'Oh, maybe I thought you deserved a little anguish over me. It's called the breaking-down process.'

'I feel so guilty that I never noticed it,' she riposted.

'Help us, Deborah, that's a lie. You just admitted it. Incidentally, I never liked it much either, but I guess it had its compensations. You're ready to fall into my arms!'

'You're way overdue for a set down!' she managed crisply.

'I wonder? Of course there won't be any present if you don't!'

She glanced at him, her green eyes half-smiling. 'That's blackmail, isn't it?'

'No, it's beautiful. What's wrong with holding hands? I really need to know everything about you.'

'And you've a considerably long way to go!'

'I know!' His glance was so disturbing that the shock held her immobile for seconds. 'What's wrong?'

'Why, nothing at all, but I've no intention of succumbing to your very experienced technique.'

'Are you so certain of that?' His voice that had slowed to a sardonic drawl suddenly picked up, his narrowed eyes against the glare of the sand mere silver chips. 'I keep forgetting you're just a child. Too young.'

'For you at any rate!'

'You've got to learn some time. I can't wait an eternity for you!' He bent down and picked up a shell, looked at it, then put it in his pocket.

'Why do you want me at all?' she demanded.

Cal straightened up and a flash of brilliance lit his eyes, making her dive away from him and run along the sand, startling a kingfisher and the brilliant lorikeets that flashed in and out of the jungle of trees, dipping long beaks into honeyed crimson bells. He was perfect for this kind of thing, but she was confused; it was no gentle awakening but a torrent of feeling that was like a physical pain. She had never believed it before, yet she wanted now to hold a hand over her heart to stop its mad racing. She had begun by telling herself that she disliked and feared him, his vitality and power, now came the supreme irony, for she knew herself to be hopelessly in love ... without hope. Whatever solutions he had worked out in his own mind, there was no suggestion that he loved her. Desired her perhaps, with a hungry physical longing, but she wanted so much more—a total merging, the language of the heart and the mind.

The freshening sea breeze was taking her breath, bending the heads of the majestic palms and the feathery casuarinas, sending the surf racing in and great white-crested sprays against the outer fringe of the reef. Inside the coral barrier the lagoon was as blue as a polished opal and as smooth, with the coral gardens in all their dazzling colours below the surface of the water. Sooty terns wheeled over one section of the water, staring down into its sparkling depths as if they were starving, then dived until they emerged with a fish. Deborah was drowning in beauty full of a fascinated tension. The pohutakawas the old man had planted many years before flared a scarlet trail right down to the beach. It was a confusion of brilliant colour and early morning serenity, the sky to the horizon a dense and cloudless blue.

Looking up at the flying buttresses of a pandanus hung with a yellow flowering creeper, she stumbled, took an incautious step to right herself, and fell over a twisted arch of the root system half buried in the sand. She toppled sideways, not hurting herself, though it looked pretty convincing as a fall, not even bothering to get up for a minute because it was so exquisite on the sand. The broad arm of a palm stretched above her and she turned over, bemused by the blue sky and the languid tilt of the palms bent to the prevailing trade winds.

Cal came up and looked down at her, his powerful lean body faultlessly poised. 'You look very nice down there. You didn't hurt yourself, did you?'

'I must get up!'

'Why bother? I'd be delighted to join you!' He sank down beside her and turned over so that he was facing her, propped up by his elbows. 'You're a funny child, provoking and withdrawing. Explain yourself, I'd like to know you better.'

'You'll have to promise to let me get to know you too!'

'What is it you want to know?' he enquired.

'Where's my present?' she asked, a smile in her eyes.

'I thought so! Actually I don't know if you're ready for it, with your hair spilling on the sand and your creamy little face slightly bemused.'

'What *is* it?'

'All right!' He swung upwards and unbuttoned his shirt pocket, withdrawing a small wad of cotton wool. 'I didn't bother wrapping it, it all adds to the cost. Anyway, if you give me your hand you'll find it's just right!'

She, too, came up in a swift movement, staring at his tanned hands. The cotton wool looked very white against his lean brown fingers, but the emerald glowed in its sunburst of diamonds, riveting her gaze and capturing her breath. Cal took her unresisting hand and slid the ring home, coolly accepting its beauty and its absolute fit. 'We'll delay the engagement party for a while, but from today onwards that's the McGovern seal of ownership. Now look me in the face and tell me what you think of it.'

Her eyes when she did face him had the turbulent brilliance of the jewel, enormous, unblinking, the tears threatening to spill as though he had done something unforgivable. 'This much I know of you, every move you make is calculated. Why me? You don't love me!'

'What's love?' His glance sparkled over her. 'Go on, you tell me!'

Deborah swept her hair back from her forehead, feeling enormously lightheaded and unable to contribute a lot. 'Has Eve Mangan got anything to do with this?' she asked.

'God, what a lunatic idea!'

'She left in a great hurry,' she pointed out.

'I suppose she did. Maybe she had an appointment too good to miss!' Cal's downbent glance was sharp with amusement.

'Don't treat me like a half-witted child!' she protested.

'And don't you treat me like a tormentor. Not at this moment. You can't escape me. Did you imagine you could?'

'I sometimes feel I can't,' she said gravely, 'then I have the minute, like now, when I feel strong. How long have you had this ring?'

'Not only the ring, but the necklace and earrings as well. I felt in a mad mood—most uncharacteristic. I'm not mean, mind you, but careful. That comes from the old man!'

'You couldn't have bought it thinking of me,' she persisted.

'Why not? What other girl I know has dark green eyes?'

She stared at him, her mind completely arrested, very young and aggrieved. 'You can't know what can happen or what's about to happen.'

'I have the second sight, inherited, plus training. I've been one step ahead for most of my life. Besides, you'll make me an admirable wife—my mind whirls at the thought. Then too, you'll give me a son—I'm not going to work for nothing. Maybe a few sons!'

'So that's it!' she said, brushing her dazzled eyes.

'Don't you want to be a part of me?'

There was a desperate hurt in her face. 'Don't you realise you're upsetting me?'

'Your voice sounds as tremulous as a bird's,' he teased.

'That's because I'm not taking any of this in and I'm not agreeing to any devilish plan of yours. I can't leave Chris and Tommy, and I could never marry a man as cold-blooded as you!'

'Thank you, I'll treasure that.' He moved swiftly and she was lying on the sand, his arm beneath her, his dark face above her hardening, his temper aroused, silver eyes flashing and ruthless. 'I can't think why you said that!'

'Because it's true,' she cried recklessly.

'True? You little fool!' He bent his head and found her mouth, forcing it open, not caring if he hurt her but gathering her ever closer to him so that she was incapable of turning her head away or hiding her soft, sensuous body from him. The single little cry she made seemed to madden him, for he lifted his head to trace his thumb over her throbbing mouth, then ran it down her throat to the lovely line of her breast. 'Don't let me hurt you.'

'I can see quite clearly that you don't love me,' she said bitterly.

'You mean because you might have to hide a few bruises? My darling girl, love isn't always kind. It isn't always gentle either. It's a mad consuming fire, or it's having that effect on me. I don't want anything between us, not even the air!'

'Then tell me you love me!' she cried.

'Isn't that what I'm doing, surely?' He lifted her face in his hands and kissed her mouth deeply, so there was nothing else for her to do but reflect his hunger. 'I love you, if you like, I don't give a damn what you call it. I definitely want to know your heart and your body and your mind. Is that love, Deborah? To feel like that for a single person? An intense illumination. If I feel like crushing you occasionally, I still want to cherish you for ever, to spare you the inevitable hurts. Anyway, you know I've wanted you from the moment I laid eyes on you!'

'Wanting isn't loving. I'm not so ignorant of the subject.'

'It's a damned good start. Some people never have what we've got now, and it's only a beginning. I'm half mad with frustration. You'll have to marry me very soon.'

'I'm afraid to,' she said, in that perfect paradise.

'Tell me why?' Cal threaded his hand through her hair.

'You have such a sweeping personality, so much temperament. All accomplishment and challenge!' she tendered almost dazedly. 'You're not giving me a chance!'

'Maybe I'm not!' he agreed dryly. 'I told you I'm no good at waiting. Can't you develop a little sweep of your own? You've plenty to work on. In fact you might be rather frightening at thirty or so!'

'I think it unlikely,' she rejoined.

His eyes were blazing, brilliantly alert, his black brows winged in his imperious dark face. 'Look at you now!' she accused him. 'You look a very dangerous man. No one in her right mind would oppose you!'

'But you're going to oppose me to the death?'

'No,' she said a little bitterly, averting her face. 'You see, I love you!'

'I hope so. Oh, I hope so.' His hands travelled over her with great sureness, then unexpectedly he bent his dark head and rested it against her breast. 'Don't fight me, Deborah, and don't look so tragic. I can't bear it. I've got everything and nothing without you!'

The weight of his head was an exquisite pain. Deborah cradled it for a moment, then laid her hand along his cheek letting it move to the nape of his neck and the strong tanned column of his throat. 'I think you do love me,' she said gently. 'I feel exactly the same. I'll even make you all the promises you want.' He went to move, but she held his head against her, his crisp black curls brushing her chin. 'No, just stay there. It's wonderful to have you my slave!'

He laughed in his throat, but it sounded tender. He relaxed a moment longer then his hand came up, turning her towards him, no longer as a slave but with the fine familiar mastery. 'I don't deserve you. Most certainly I don't deserve you!'

'Perhaps not,' she said softly, 'but I haven't the strength to resist you. Hi, my love. Lover-to-be!'

'Hi!' his smile was like quicksilver lighting his face. 'If you had just one wish in the world, what would it be?'

'That we would live out our lives together. That we would learn to love each other even more deeply. Not only now with all the radiance we're feeling, but through all the long years and the times of crisis. A love that would be our purpose and personal triumph!'

Cal looked at her searchingly, then he bent and kissed her mouth as a tribute. 'We'll make it. I'll be there and you'll be there and we have all the will in the world!'

'Then there's no better answer,' she smiled. 'Right now it's an agony just waiting for you to kiss me again!'

He moved his hand casually until she saw his eyes. Then with a little moan of wonder she pulled his head down to her with her own tantalising surge of initiative, delighting him with the realisation of the depth of passion she had tried so hard to keep from him. 'I'll never let you go,' he said tautly, 'I mean that!'

The emerald flashed on her hand and she turned it to the light. 'Thank you for my ring. It's very beautiful and very valuable, I know. Thank you for everything, but most of all thank you for being *you*!'

'Don't thank me. *Marry* me!' he said urgently.

'That's all?'

'I'll accept that for a start,' he murmured gently, stroking her cheek with tender possessive fingers.

'So will I.'

She closed her eyes and felt his mouth sink on her own. The palms drew a veil around them, and above and around them the wind song sang in their ears.

# Harlequin
# Announces the
# COLLECTION
# EDITIONS
# OF 1978

Harlequin's Collection 12

ANDREA BLAKE
**Night of the Hurrica**

Harlequin's Collection 106    1.25

ANNE WEALE
**If This Is Love**

## stories of special
## beauty and significance

# 25 Beautiful stories of particular merit

In 1976 we introduced the first 100 Harlequin Collections — a selection of titles chosen from our best sellers of the past 20 years. This series, a trip down memory lane, proved how great romantic fiction can be timeless and appealing from generation to generation. Perhaps because the theme of love and romance is eternal, and, when placed in the hands of talented, creative, authors whose true gift lies in their ability to write from the heart, the stories reach a special level of brilliance that the passage of time cannot dim. Like a treasured heirloom, an antique of superb craftsmanship, a beautiful gift from someone loved, — these stories too, have a special significance that transcends the ordinary.

# Here's your 1978 Harlequin Collection Editions . . .

More great Harlequin 1978 Collection Editions . . .

**122 Moon Over Africa**
*Pamela Kent*
(#983)

**123 Island In The Dawn**
*Averil Ives*
(#984)

**124 Lady In Harley Street**
*Anne Vinton*
(#985)

**125 Play The Tune Softly**
*Amanda Doyle*
(#1116)

**126 Will You Surrender?**
*Joyce Dingwell*
(#1179)

**Original Harlequin Romance numbers in brackets**

Offer expires December 31, 1978

# Send for your copy today!

# The Harlequin Romance Catalog FREE!

Here's your chance to catch up on all the wonderful Harlequin Romance novels you may have missed because the books are no longer available at your favorite booksellers.

Complete the coupon and mail it to us. By return mail, we'll send you a copy of the latest Harlequin catalog. Then you'll be able to order the books you want directly from us.

*Clip and mail coupon today.*

# Remember when a good love story made you feel like holding hands?

Harlequin presents

# LEOPARD
## in the
# SNOW
### ...a love story